D1615943

Growing Up in The Ville in St. Louis, MO

Pauline Estelle Merry

Great Tales Told Well Publishing

9472 Central Ave., Garden Grove, CA 92844-1505

This book is about a real person and her family. The historical figures, individuals directly related to the author and public notables of The Ville who are mentioned herein are described accurately insofar as the author can recall. All other persons are from the imagination of the author, and any resemblance of them to other persons living or dead is purely coincidental.

Growing Up in The Ville in St. Louis, MO
First Edition November 2022 ISBN 979-8-9871997-0-1

Printed in the United States of America

Dedication & Acknowledgements

Dedicated to:

My parents, Pauline Stricklin Merry and Frederick Luther Merry. Two truly extraordinary people.

My profound thanks:

I first want thank my grandson, Aaron Hegamin. I can't remember how many times he said to me, "Pauli, your life is a great story. Why don't you write a book about it?" Well, Aaron, here it is!

And, I must thank John M. Goodman, my husband. He was my go-to computer person. He created the book's design. He questioned my thinking on hundreds of ideas. He was my cheerleader and so much more. Truly, this book would not have happened without his love and support.

And my editors, Ann Perrah & John Lunsford, *The Book-Writer's Midwives*. Every author should have them in their corner. Their opinions mattered and I was wise enough to listen to them.

Liz Trapp not only read an early draft, she also read very closely a near-final draft and applied her extraordinary talents as a copy editor to help save me from embarrassing myself with easily preventable errors.

Thanks also to Valena Broussard Dismukes, another of my steadfast early readers. Her feedback was most appreciated.

I also thank all the other wonderful people in my life who have lovingly supported me in all of my endeavors.

You know who you are.

Table of Contents

Prologue

One summer when I was about ten, I went with my parents and my sister to Boston to visit the relatives of my father's first wife, Jackie Jackson. She was only the third Negro woman to graduate from Radcliff College in 1919. We were in Boston at a busy, busy intersection where I, trying to keep up with everybody, started to cross the street. Just then a car came toward me, almost hitting me, but a slight, white young man pushed me to safety as the car sped by. I was surprised, but thankful that I was now out of danger. The man took off too quickly for us to thank him. My mother turned to me and said, "Pauline Estelle, that man saved your life. I believe you were spared because you were meant to be here and do something important."

The stories in this book are about me, Pauline Estelle, a young colored girl growing up in the 40s and 50s in St. Louis, MO in an area called The Ville. Where I lived was safe, the houses and streets were well kept, neighbors looked out for one another. And there was everything there—churches, a movie house, Billy Burkes (our local eatery), the Poro Hotel, the Annie Malone Orphan's Home, the Turner School for disabled children, an elementary school, the high school, a college, and a well-regarded hospital. Each of my stories finds me exploring my world, how I fit, and how I could get along.

I lived with my Father, Frederick Luther Merry (I called him Daddy, but his friends called him Merry, and my mother called him Fritz), my Mother, Pauline Stricklin Merry (I called her Mother, but Daddy called her Pleen), and my younger sister, Frederica (we all called her Freddie). We had no relatives who lived in the city or anywhere close, so it was just the four of us. I have no nickname and I do not like either of my names, especially Estelle, but I am stuck with them.

I was not a pretty or a cute girl, but I was smart, inquisitive, and fearless. In this book, you'll spend time with

1

me as I use my mind to solve problems, navigate my way in school, my family, and community, and just be a skinny, dark-skinned, nappy-headed kid.

What you just read was my younger self speaking—and that is most of what you'll hear throughout this book. But from time to time, you'll hear from me as an adult (now in my eighties, retired and living in Garden Grove, California with my third husband, after a long career as a top-level administrator in the California Community College System), occasionally commenting on things my younger-self just told you. Over my lifetime I've learned a lot, and I want you to know some of those things.

For example, I'll tell you a bit about history, laws, and practices like the "Jim Crow" laws that were a part of my everyday life and the lives of all Negroes living in the United States. (I use the terms colored, Black, and Negro interchangeably.)

At the end of each story I've put a few questions. I hope you'll think about them, and decide what your answers to them are.

My hope is that you'll be inspired by these stories and that you will seek challenges, explore places near and far and, most of all, learn not to be afraid.

* * * * *

In my stories I mention of a lot of places. You may wonder where they are. So, to help you, I've included four maps. The first map, "My Ville," shows you many of the places you'll read about that were close to my home. The next map, "My St. Louis," shows some of the places in greater St. Louis that I went to. The third map, "My Country," shows you other places in the United States that show up in my stories. The last map, "My World," shows you some of those places and some others outside my country.

Story 1
Kindergarten Through Eighth Grade

My name is Pauline Estelle. I have chocolate-colored skin and nappy hair that has to be straightened with a hot comb. My mother had aspirations for me and my sister Freddie that went beyond our just going to school and church. But I will talk about all that later. For now, this is where my first story for you begins, in 1942.

I liked going to school. When I would hear people say that they did not like school, I had the hardest time understanding that. What was not to like? Teachers? Well maybe sometimes, but most of the time I looked up to them. In my elementary schools they were all women. Not a man to be seen, except for the stern principal and the helpful janitor. Classmates? Well, some I liked and some I didn't. Those who liked me, mostly I also liked them. Those who didn't like me, I stayed away from. I learned to read fast, and I loved that reading was a handy way for me to be in other worlds and places and to learn new things. I read books that were way over my head, like *Kon-Tiki* by Thor Heyerdahl, and found them exciting as they stretched my mind and imagination.

There were other things that made school special, like the smells of the classroom with their chalk, paste, other people's clothes and bodies, and the musty closet where the teacher kept her supplies. All of these things were distracting, mysterious, and sometimes even scary. This story is about my going to school, the center of my world.

Kindergarten

"No, Mrs. Merry, you have to go to the back of the line."

Simmons School was a segregated school and it was the first elementary school I went to in St. Louis.

My mother had marched us to the front of the line on my very first day of school. I remember it so clearly, I was wearing a yellow starched cotton sailor blouse and skirt. The top had a sailor collar with white stripes on it. The skirt was pleated. Mother was wearing a pretty yellow dress as well, one that buttoned to the waist.

Simmons Elementary School

When Mother walked us to the front of the line, even at five years old, I knew that she had done something wrong and I was embarrassed, even though I didn't know one person in the line. She then took me by the hand and we went to the back of the line. Shortly, we again arrived at the front of the line, and I was duly enrolled in Kindergarten at Simmons Elementary School, where I spent the next six years.

Recently, when taking a nostalgic trip to The Ville, I saw a FOR SALE sign on the Simmons School building. How could a school building be for sale, I asked myself, but of course I knew the answer. The Ville had been abandoned. North St. Louis, where The Ville is located, had become a mere shadow of its former, vital self. Vacant lots, houses boarded up. No people walking about. No children playing in yards. No one sitting on their front porch.

There is a long, long history behind this decline. St. Louis' government structure goes back many years. The city proper is surrounded by sixteen—yes, sixteen—separate, independent municipalities. They include Clayton, Richmond Heights, Webster, Overland and Ferguson—yes, that Ferguson[1]. As whites fled to the county from the city, colored people left The Ville and moved into neighborhoods that the whites had left.

---

[1] You may have heard of this town, since in 2014 a local and a national outcry arose after a young Black man was killed there by a white policeman.

Over the years, many plans to revitalize The Ville have been tossed around, but nothing has been accomplished. One important opportunity was lost when the light rail system was built. Its route seemed to intentionally skirt The Ville. The resulting lack of transportation in and out of the area could not help but contribute to its decline. So, what I saw on my visit was far from the wonderful Ville of my childhood.

In spite of being forced to live in segregated communities, many colored communities thrived. Their residents lived full, rich, interesting lives. This had been the case of life in The Ville back then, but no longer. And when the residents left, they took with them those feelings of community, the actions of caring, and commitment to bettering the lives of its people.

While I was not totally surprised to see the For Sale sign on my elementary school, I felt somehow betrayed by the forces that insist on trying to keep Black folks "in their place."

As long as I was a kindergartner, my mother walked me to school every morning and picked me up at noon. I loved walking with her and my little sister.

"Look at the flowers in Mrs. Nesby's yard, Pauline Estelle, Beautiful, aren't they?"

And, trying to keep up with my mother, I would say things like, "Oh look, Mother, see how Mr. Prince has painted his front door dark green. I like that color."

We looked at the buildings and the flowers. We made up stories about the people we saw going into the hospital, or the Annie Malone Orphan's home. "I wonder if that little girl will go back to her parents?" Sometimes we would toss a penny into the air and when it fell on the sidewalk, if it was heads, we would go to the right; if it was tails, we would go to the left. The 'penny walk,' as we called it, gave us a way to change where and how far we might walk, when we didn't want to do the same old thing every day.

We enjoyed the change of weather from fall through the winter and into spring, with leaves going from green to orange and yellow to no leaves on the trees at all. And from wearing no sweaters to heavy wool winter garments with mittens, and back to light sweaters again. It was wonderful to be with my mother who made walking to and from school such fun. And, because of our walks and what I learned in kindergarten, I looked forward to going to first grade. I also started piano lessons with Miss Myrtle Burgess.

First Grade

"Yes, Mrs. Merry," my teacher, Miss Jackson, said to my mother, "Pauline Estelle has learned to read in record time."

Dick and Jane were my early reading "partners in crime" in the world of reading. Their white skin, yellow hair and blue eyes were the only inhabitants of the pages in the reader. I never thought to question their presence in it, just as I didn't question the absence of Black children in it, either. And though the book seemed a bit ragged—perhaps it was a hand-me down from a white school—we did have books. I still have strong memories of them. "See Dick run. See Jane play. See Dick and Jane run and play." Reading came easily to me. Letters of the alphabet made words. Words made sentences. Sentences became paragraphs. Paragraphs became stories. Give me a book and I was in heaven!

My first grade teacher was a pretty woman. She was single, because women teachers weren't allowed to be married. She wore her long hair in two braids wrapped around her head. Although she was colored, she could have passed for white, and I wondered why she didn't. Passing was an opportunity to get out of the meanness of segregation, and I had supposed that since she could have passed, she would have. I knew some people who were passing. I knew they were Black, but I knew I shouldn't talk to them when I saw them on the bus.

I read about a woman who disappeared in to the white world, giving instructions to her Black family to never ever contact her again. While I don't recall exactly what I read, I imagine that she wrote them a letter saying something like this:

"My Dear Family, I am tired of having to step off sidewalks when white folks walk by. I am tired of not being able to live where I want, or eat in restaurants, or to have to go to segregated schools. I'm tired of not being able to try on clothes in a department store. I'm tired of not being able to get a job other than that of a maid. I'm tired of being an invisible, second class person, because that is the nature of living in a segregated world—a world of restriction after restriction after restriction. And so it is with a heavy heart that I must ask you never to contact me again. Being white in this country is, by far, much easier than being colored. I will miss you, but I know that you'll understand my decision."

I am sure that they did not contact her again, with great sadness, but also with acceptance.

As for my teacher, I wished that I looked like her, but even though she was pretty, I perceived a sadness about her that I didn't understand and can't explain. She seemed lonely to me. When I would pass her on the sidewalk after school, she would wave and smile at me from across the street. I had no idea where she lived, but I would have loved to have visited her on my own after school.

Naturally, I made up stories about my teacher's life. I imagined that she lived in a pretty house, and that she had come from somewhere in Alabama and that she had gone to a teacher's college there. In all of the stories I made up about her, except for the sadness, she had a perfect life with family and friends.

Second Grade

"Mrs. Merry, the other second grade teacher Miss Taylor, the principal, Mr. Norris and I have conferred and we agree that Pauline Estelle should skip the second half of the second grade."

Other than getting promoted one semester, I cannot recall anything else memorable about that half-year I spent in second grade. So that was it for me with the second grade!

Third Grade

"Mrs. Merry, Pauline Estelle needs help with cursive writing. I am giving you some lined paper. Will you please see that she uses it to help her practice and catch up with the other students who got started on cursive writing in the second half of the second grade?"

The Palmer Method was used to teach cursive writing and, although my mother worked with me, my handwriting never was as pretty as hers, or my father's, until many years later.

In spite of having fallen behind in cursive writing, I loved the third grade. I don't recall missing any of the other students that I left behind and immediately fell into what my new classmates were learning. I made new friends easily. One of them was Betty Owens. People said that we looked alike. We both wore glasses, were almost the same shade of brown, had hair that had to be pressed and curled. So we pretended that we were sisters, even though she had a baby brother and I had a younger sister. She and I were tight. I would call to her as I passed by her house in the mornings on my way to Simmons, or she might be waiting for me as I passed by, and we would walk together, with other kids joining us along the way. Shirley Carslick, Emma Young, Carlene Townsend, and some boys whose names I didn't bother to learn, because they were...boys.

The walk from my house on St. Ferdinand went past the Sumner High School schoolyard, across the west end of

Tandy Park, past the tennis courts, Stowe Teachers College and Turner School. There was a short sidewalk that went right past the apartment court where Betty lived. The area outside Betty's apartment had a curious smell: a mixture of oats and some sort of flower I couldn't identify, but it was memorable, distinctive and fragrant. Interesting, the things one remembers. We also met other children along the way and then shortly, we arrived at Simmons.

The few times I saw them, Betty's parents looked very young, I wondered about them. Who were they? Were they new to St. Louis? These are thoughts that were never fully formed in my mind, but I did wonder where they had come from. And why?

That was a pretty important question for me to have thought of at that age, and it would be years before I found out the answer. All I knew at that time was what I saw, and what I saw was that Betty's parents were also much younger than my parents and were probably not college graduates.

In Story 3, "Where Have You Been" I'll explain how I decided to find at least some answer for myself, and how that answer was useful to others. And in Story 5, "Sumner High School" you'll find out how I learned a more complete answer.

My parents had grey hair, while none of my friends' parents did, and that was an embarrassment to me. Both of my parents had been married to other partners before they met and married one another and had me and my sister. My father's first wife had gone to Radcliff College in Boston. Both she and my father were English teachers who had tried to teach in the South, but having been born and raised in the North, they found the South unacceptable in many ways.

My mother majored in Home Economics at Pratt Institute in Brooklyn (a borough in New York city). Her first husband was a physician whom she met and married while they both worked at Harlem Hospital (in Manhattan, another borough in New York City). They had one child, my older sister, Betty Jane. They divorced, and shortly thereafter my mother gave Betty Jane to my Aunt Irene to raise.

By the time my parents met, married and had my sister and me, they were considered old. In fact, what I would often say about a new friend's mother was, "And her mother is young," a statement that, in hindsight, probably hurt my mother's feelings.

My piano lessons were coming along. I loved taking the bus to Miss Burgess' house on Page Avenue on Saturday mornings during the school year for my lessons. I took summers off. The red *John Thompson* music books that I played from had drawings of kids doing various things, and the pieces were supposed to accompany those activities. Miss Burgess had a small black baby grand piano; I practiced at home on a large brown upright piano that was near our front door. You couldn't miss it. That was the piano I practiced on from the time I started playing until I stopped taking lessons when I turned fourteen. Even though she didn't read music, my mother regularly sat at my side as I practiced. She often praised me, adding that she wished that she had learned to play. I enjoyed her company. It was our time together.

Once again, I was skipped a half grade.

Fourth Grade

"Mrs. Merry, is everything alright at home? Pauline Estelle has worn the same green striped taffeta dress for almost a week, she seems a little sad, and her classroom work is not up to her usual high level."

I didn't realize that a teacher sending a note home asking my mother a question like that was very unusual for a teacher in the '40s. In my classes, my teachers' jobs were to teach reading, writing, arithmetic, history, some art, some geography and, if we were lucky, some music. My friends and I were called pupils, and our teachers were not expected to be experts in much of anything outside of the subjects just mentioned, and they certainly were not expected to probe into the lives of their pupils beyond what they could do inside a classroom.

Counselors, teacher aids, special help for disabled students, foreign languages, subject matter specialists, all of the specialized subject areas and pupil resources did not happen until parents began to demand services for their children with special needs. Then the expansion of services for all students occurred. (This is a curious phenomenon called the "cut curve effect": when conditions for a particular group are improved, those improvements also benefit others.) None of my teachers would recognize a twenty-first century elementary school curriculum, as it is far richer than anyone could have imagined back then. On the other hand, they don't teach cursive writing nowadays. I guess trade-offs are inevitable.

I guess, like most children, I had no idea what the relationship was between my mother and father. I knew that there was tension between them, and I knew that they argued. I knew that money was tight, even though we didn't feel poor. I felt that my mother was not a happy woman and that my father probably was not a happy man.

This was why I liked going to visit my Aunt and Uncle in Chestertown, Maryland in the summer so much. It was a respite for me from my tense family life in St. Louis.

I did not really like my father, even though he was smart, respected in the community, well educated, as were both of my parents. Nevertheless, I thought that he was mean, and I was afraid of him.

Once he beat me really hard for some small infraction that I never really understood. I never forgave him. I had to be in bed for two days to recover from the beating. I wondered what mother thought about it, and why she didn't stop him. This has always been a mystery to me. I remember seeing her peek at me from outside the room where I lay recovering from the beating. She never said a word to me or reprimanded him, as far as I know.

The truth is I really wanted my parents to divorce so that my mother would leave him and go back to Chestertown, Maryland. My ideal father would be a man like my Uncle Ben who was married to my mother's oldest sister, Irene. I admired and envied their relationship. They laughed and talked together all the time, and I especially loved hearing them talking late at night. She would say, "Ben, now let me talk." He would laugh and say, "Okay Irene, your turn." I never, ever heard my parents play with each other like that, and I wished that they had. My Aunt and Uncle seemed to just plain *like* each other. And although she was twenty years his senior, they were married for over 50 years.

My fourth grade teacher correctly sensed that something was not right in my home, but little changed in my life even after her inquiry. I suppose things got better between my parents, but I never will know for sure. They stayed married and lived out their lives together.

My life outside of school was not particularly exciting or interesting. Weekdays I went to school and back, Saturdays I went to my piano lessons, and on Sundays I went to church. Nothing at all unusual. Just a little girl in a small family with small family pursuits...a lovely phrase.

A truly marvelous thing happened when I was in the fourth grade. The Bookmobile of the St. Louis Public Library System began to make scheduled visits to The Ville. It took me a while to figure out the schedule of where it would be and when. Sometimes it would park right out in front of my house. Other times it would be parked somewhere else in The Ville, like Tandy Park or near some church. And what would a little girl like me who loved words and who loved to read think about the Bookmobile?

Nothing, other than that there was a heaven, and that sometimes it even parked at my front door!

I suppose that because my parents were well-educated, the English spoken in my household was grammatically correct and I was accustomed to hearing big words when they spoke to each other and to their friends. When I didn't understand a word's meaning, I would ask and either my mother or father would give me a definition. We had conversations about word meanings and word usage. I don't recall using a dictionary much to look up word meanings. I would just infer what I thought they meant. But then, those were the kinds of words that I deliberately added to my vocabulary. My mother had invested in a set of *World Book Encyclopedia,* about which she would say to me, "Go look it up," when even she didn't know something.

The bookmobile provided me ready access to books, books, and more books, and it was free! I liked learning new words and I got the reputation of showing off when I used them, especially in the classroom. I was not particularly popular because of that, but I didn't let my lack of popularity stop me from finding and then using "big" words. Using them correctly made me feel special. One time at a classroom election, when nominated for some position (which I didn't want), I said, "I decline." I was so thrilled with myself. I had used a word that no other kid in the class had ever used. Some turned their heads toward me and frowned. I didn't care.

It was perhaps because of my feeling of superiority about my use of big words that I got into a fight with some girl whose name I can't remember. For some reason, she and I were egged on to a fight which had been brewing for several days. Finally, that day we met in the poorly-lit girl's bathroom in the basement and had our fight. And even though I lost—I was knocked down and had a bruise on my arm where she hit me—the fight had little impact on my relations with my friends. No teacher intervened, and of course I never told my parents. In fact, other than those who were present that day, you are the first to know about it.

Fifth Grade

"Mrs. Merry," my teacher said to her, "A group of girls in the class have expressed an interest in becoming Brownie Scouts. Do you think that you might be their Brownie Scout Troop Leader?"

And, much to my surprise, my mother said, "Why yes, I would."

Our troop had the smallest number of members that were required—ten—Frances, Nadine, Betty, Laura, Mary Carolyn, Nanette, Elizabeth, Mattie, Shirley and me. My sister, Freddie, was too young to be an official member, but she participated in most all of our activities, making for eleven in our troop. And what was even more surprising was

Pauline Estelle with Brownies

that my mother really enjoyed being our leader. We wore the brown uniform and she wore the grown-up version of the same dress. She did not have any formal training to be a scout leader. She mostly made up activities for us to do, using the chapters from the Girl Scout Handbook.

She enlisted Frances' mother, Mrs. Denny, to teach us how to knit and crochet. I never got crocheting down, but I could knit like an expert. My mother taught us a little about food groups and cooking. With her Home Economics degree from Pratt Institute, she had worked as a Dietitian at Harlem Hospital. She used her knowledge of food groups and healthy eating when she taught "her little Brownies," as she liked to call us, about food and nutrition. We learned to cook smothered chicken, lima beans and—her favorite dessert—

lemon meringue pie. We tried to make a garden in my back yard, but that was an absolute failure. We collected scrap metal for the war effort, but finding a way to deliver it was next to impossible. Mostly, she made up activities for our weekly meetings. And we learned a bit about personal safety.

There was a story in the Handbook that fascinated me about camping, but that was so out of our reach that we didn't attempt to do anything with it. In that story there was a drawing of a hatchet. I was so enamored of it, that I bought one with the few dollars I had saved. Whatever happened to it, I'll never know, but owning it satisfied some vague dream that I had about camping, such as chopping down trees, making paths, using it as a weapon—that sort of thing.

Many years later, I did a lot of car camping and that long-ago camping dream was finally fulfilled, although I did it without a hatchet.

I would have loved to have learned about survival skills, but that, too, was out of my mother's reach. One highlight of the year was that with the help of Frances' mother, Mrs. Denny, we went on an outing to the Forest Park Zoo. Another weirdness about St. Louis was that Black people could go to the Forest Park Zoo without the repressive restrictions or a special day just for us, because it was a city owned facility. While next door, the amusement park, a privately owned facility, was off limits and didn't allow Blacks to attend on any day. Even though I became accustomed to these restrictions, they were still restrictions which couldn't help but have a negative effect on how I thought about myself. Yet on some level, I knew that enduring segregation somehow made me strong. I could survive and make my own way. In my mind, I was able to make "lemonade," my nice life, out of the "lemons" of segregation.

Our little Brownie troop had fun getting together, wearing our uniforms and learning odd bits and pieces about this and that. Our troop lasted for one year. After that, none of us had any interest in continuing it.

My Brownie Scout experience is a fond memory. Had I continued into Girl Scouts, I would have joined a distinguished company, that included Queen Latifah, Dionne Warwick, Condoleezza Rice, Star Jones, Jackie Joyner-Kersee, and Venus Williams.

Then came a very significant change in our lives. My parents bought a fourplex apartment building on Hammett Place. Our moving there meant that I would have to transfer in the middle of the semester to a different elementary school, Cote Brilliante.

4718 Hammet Place

I said good-bye to Miss Davis, my teacher, and my Simmons School friends, and our house on St. Ferdinand in The Ville.

Sixth Grade

"Welcome, Mrs. Merry to Cote Brilliante Elementary School. We wonder if you'd like to serve on the PTA?" My mother declined the request. "Perhaps later," she said. "We are new to the neighborhood. Please give us a little time to get acquainted, and perhaps I will be able to participate at a later time." She never did.

I loved my new school. The school had a much prettier exterior than did Simmons. While Simmons looked like a school made out of bricks stacked one on top of the other, Cote Brilliante's

Cote Brilliante Elementary School

design had a more classic look, a beautifully manicured front lawn, with a spacious play yard behind it. It was also a bit closer to my new home than Simmons had been to our house on St. Ferdinand, making my walk to school shorter.

We were among the first Black families to move west from The Ville into a neighborhood that had previously been occupied only by whites. Typically, housing in St. Louis was completely segregated, with neighborhoods for whites and other neighborhoods for colored. There were white people still living on our street where we had moved, including in three of the apartments in our new home. But, after a year or so, all of the white families had moved "out to the county." a phrase which means they went to one of the several cities outside St. Louis city limits, but still in St. Louis county.

Racism was the dominant social factor that garnered our attention and affected all of our lives..

This was 'white flight.' Blacks move in; whites move out. All sorts of attitudes and practices cause this to happen, but primarily whites were told that the property values would go down if Blacks moved in. And perhaps more importantly, we weren't considered equal human beings to whites.

Even today, segregationists' attitudes persist and school children still feel the effects of segregation in public schools and these effects will continue as long as people live where they live. Where a kid goes to school, except for busing, depends on where you live. And although the 1954 Brown vs. Board of Education Supreme Court ruling technically ended segregated schools, de facto segregation continues to this day.

When the Brown vs. Board of Education came down, I was 17. Sitting in my chemistry class I remember Mr. Knowling saying, "Don't think that you all are going to be going to school with whites, because you aren't." He was right.

And so, on Hammett Place white friends and colored friends passed each other as we went to our respective, segregated schools. Yet after school, we played together. Well, we did, until all of the white kids moved away.

Grade Seven

"Mrs. Merry, we are doing a history story about traveling to foreign countries and Pauline Estelle says that you and Mr. Merry went to England and France just before World War II. Would you be willing to come and tell the class a bit about your travels there?"

Surprisingly, my mother said, "Why yes, I would." I could never predict when she would say 'yes' or 'no' when a decision involving others was required.

I knew that my father had been to Europe before, serving as a medic in France during World War I. His trip there with my mother was the second time he had been abroad. After World War II, President Harry Truman integrated the military. But, of course when my father served, Black men and women were in units segregated from whites.

After he and my mother married, they sailed on the *Isle de France* to Europe for their honeymoon. They spent some time in London, then, together, they made their way to Paris, France. He left her there and bravely went to Berlin to see Jesse Owens run in the 1936 Olympics.

My father told me that at those 1936 Olympics in Berlin, Owens won four gold medals, in the 100m, 200m, 4x100m relay and the long jump. He broke or equaled nine Olympic records and also set three world records. One of those world records was in the 4x100m relay. These wins wouldn't be bettered for 20 years.

And my father, along with Adolf Hitler, was there and so both of them were witnesses to Owen's success.

Meanwhile on her own, back in Paris, my mother became an adventurer. She ate at sidewalk cafes, strolled the Left Bank of the Seine, walked along the Right Bank, window-shopped, visited the Eiffel Tower, the L'Arc de Triomphe, the Louvre, and the Montmartre Cemetery. She went to hear some black musicians in Paris' Lower Montmartre, which was known as Black Montmartre. Because she was colored, the people who went to hear the musicians thought that she was with the musicians. She found that misperception quite amusing and pretended that she was part of the musician's group and they, in turn, allowed her to sit on or near the stage as she drank "un petit verre de vin."

This is what she told my fascinated classmates and teachers who dropped into the classroom to hear her talk. She had dressed the part, wearing a beautiful black cloche with a short veil. A black short jacket was worn over her black wool dress. Her shoes were stylish. And of course she had on black gloves. I was so proud that my mother had been to Paris, while most of my teachers had hardly been out of Missouri.

Many years later I also went to Paris, doing the grand European tour with my oldest sister. As we were flying into New York City after a wonderful time in Europe, a feeling of dread and oppression descended over me. I was returning to the country of my birth, where I wasn't wanted or valued.

Grade Eight

"Mrs. Merry, for the eight grade graduation, we would like Pauline Estelle to provide the musical selection for the program. Will you allow her to play the piano that morning?"

My mother turned to me and asked, "Would you like to do that, Pauline Estelle?"

I was scared to play, but I also was afraid to say no, so I said, "Okay, I will do it."

On the morning of the graduation, my mother and I each wore light blue dresses, short navy blue jackets and black patent shoes, but it was cloudy and it looked as though it might rain. My mother, who was big on praying, said to me that she had prayed that it wouldn't rain, but then laughed at herself when she carried an umbrella along—just in case. I played Edward McDowell's *To A Wild Rose*, a piece my piano teacher said was his best known composition.

My elementary school career ended on a successful note as I loved going to school, being considered smart, and feeling self-confident. I liked my teachers, being in a classroom, and reading. I was successful in all of the subjects that we studied, and I made some life-long friends. I felt safe, happy, and "respected," an odd word for a thirteen year old to use to describe herself, but it fit for me. But, in spite of feeling safe, I was aware of the limitations put upon my race in this country and these limitations are in the fabric of everything that is American.

Below I have quoted a document from 1898 that describes a formidable mindset that Negroes have had to endure ever since 1619. It is called the white Man's Declaration of Independence. Read it and you may understand some of what colored people in this country have had to live through. I am including it because most people in the US have not had the history of slavery taught to them. This piece will give you an idea of how and what we have endured in our public and private lives.

On November 09, 1898, some 33 years after the Civil War, a meeting of the most prominent white citizens was held at the Courthouse in Wilmington, North Carolina because they were upset that a Negro printer (a Mr. Manly) had the temerity to publish a newspaper for his (Black) community.

At the meeting, one of those incensed whites, a Mr. Waddell, stood up and read the "White Man's Declaration of Independence" which called for the expulsion of Editor Manly and his printing press.

White Man's Declaration of Independence

Believing that the Constitution of the United States contemplated a government to be carried on by an enlightened people.

Believing that its framers did not anticipate the enfranchisement of an ignorant population of African origin, and believing that those men of the State of North Carolina, who joined in forming the Union, did not contemplate for their descendants' subjection to an inferior race.

We, the undersigned citizens of the City of Wilmington and County of New Hanover, do hereby declare that we will no longer be ruled, and will never again be ruled by men of African origin.

This condition we have in part endured because we felt that the consequences of the War of Secession were such as to deprive us of the fair consideration of many of our countrymen. We believe that, after more than thirty years, this is no longer the case.

The stand we now pledge ourselves to is forced upon us suddenly by a crisis and our eyes are open to the fact that we must act now or leave our descendants to a fate too gloomy to submit.

We therefore, believing that we represent unequivocally the sentiment of the White People of the County and City, hereby for ourselves, and as representing them, proclaim:

First

That the time has passed for the intelligent citizens of the community owning 90% of the property and paying taxes in like proportions, to be ruled by negroes.

Second

That we will not tolerate the action of unscrupulous white men in affiliating with the negroes so that means of their votes they can dominate the intelligent and thrifty element in the community, thus causing business to stagnate and progress to be out of the question.

Third

That the negro has demonstrated by antagonizing our interest in every way, and especially by his ballot, that he is incapable of realizing that his interests are and should be identical with those of the community.

Fourth

That the progressive element in any community is the white population and that the giving of nearly all the employment to negro laborers has been against the best interests of this County and City and is a sufficient reason why the City of Wilmington, with its natural advantages has not become a city of at least fifty thousand inhabitants.

Fifth

That we propose in future to give to white men a large part of the employment heretofore given to negroes because we realize that white families cannot thrive here unless there are more opportunities for the employment of the different members of said families.

Sixth

That the white men expect to live in this community peaceably; to have and provide absolute protection for their families, who shall be safe from insult or injury from all persons, whomsoever. We are prepared to treat the negroes with justice and consideration in all matters which do not involve sacrifices of the interest of the intelligent and progressive portion of the community. But are equally prepared now and immediately to enforce what we know to be our rights.

Seventh

That we have been, in our desire for harmony and peace, blinded both to our best interests and our rights. A climax was reached when the negro paper of this city published an article so vile and slanderous that it would in most communities have resulted in the lynching of the editor. We deprecate lynching and yet there is no punishment, provided by the courts, adequate for this offense. We therefore owe it to the people of this community and of this city, as a protection against such license in the future, that the paper known as the "Record" cease to be published and that its editor be banished from this community.

We demand that he leave this City forever within twenty-four hours after the issuance of this proclamation. Second, that the printing press from which the "Record" has been issued be packed and shipped from the City without delay, that we be notified within twelve hours of the acceptance or rejection of this demand. If the demand is agreed to, within twelve hours we counsel forbearance on the part of all white men. If the demand is refused or if no answer within the time mentioned then the editor, Manly, will be expelled by force.

This outrageous statement had the authority of whiteness to back it up. Now, at the wonderful age of 85, I am living in a new awareness and new appreciation and new outspokenness. This time feels like a new time for Blacks in this country and I am happy to be able to experience it. White people were in control, and have been in control and set the rules of behavior since this country was born. Now in 2022, these rules are being challenged in a way that is an extension of the civil rights era, and this challenge is even more powerful, less fearful, more self-authoritative, less asking for permission. And I like the feel of it. It is like a third wave of Black expression and Black civil rights. I think those that came before would be happily surprised and proud of the tenor of these times.

＊ ＊ ＊ ＊ ＊

Some Questions to Think About

1. Do you enjoy reading? What's your favorite book so far? Why?

2. What do you like most about school? What do you like the least? What is your favorite subject?

3. How many different places have you lived so far? How many different schools have you attended? What is your most interesting class ever?

4. Do you feel safe in your neighborhood? Why or why not?

5. What has someone taught you how to *do*, outside of school? Like knitting, gardening, building something, etc. What would you really like to learn how to do?

6. Are you lucky enough to speak and understand more than one language? What language (or languages) would you like to learn? Why?

7. Have you or your parents ever traveled to a foreign country? Has anyone in your family come here from another country?

8. If you could travel to anywhere in the world, where would you go, and why? What would you plan to see or do there?

9. What is something special or unique about *you*? And, what is something special you see in a good friend?

10. Has reading my first story inspired you to try something new or different for yourself? If so, what is it? And how are you imagining yourself making it happen?

If You Want to Learn More
Here is one good source of information:

Emmett J. Scott. Scott's Official History of the American Negro in the World War, 1919. New York: Arno Press, 1969. Humanities and Social Sciences Division, Library of Congress (7–2)

I'd love to hear from you, my readers.
You may contact me, the author, by emailing
me at:
PaulineEstelleMerry@GreatTalesToldWell.com

Map: "My Ville"

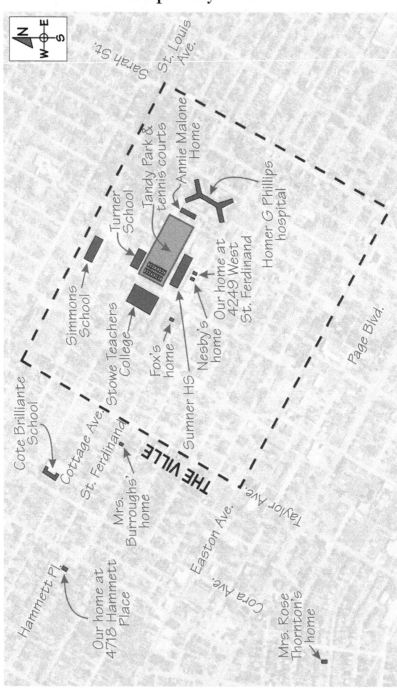

Story 2
Seeing 'The Greats' with My Mother

My parents, especially my mother, were determined to expose my sister and me to everything that was educational, artistic, and musical within their means. So I had wonderful experiences outside of my home, experiences that brought worlds of beauty, mystery, art and music into what might have been just an ordinary little colored girl's life. My mother saw to it. The events in this story happened between 1945 and 1952.

* * * * *

My mother started me on the piano when I was five years old. My first teacher was Miss Myrtle Burgess, who was one of the black elite of St. Louis. Her claim to fame was a mention of herself in a book about prominent Black people in the city. I remember her as being short, round, light-skinned and having brown hair. She was pleasant, smiled easily, and wore a uniform of dark-colored rayon dresses that buttoned down the front, from the neck to the hem. She had a shiny black baby grand in her small living room where she taught our lessons.

Those lessons came out of the John Thompson music books which are still produced today. I enjoyed my lessons but, as I look back, I don't think that Miss Burgess or my other two teachers, Mrs. Ward and Mrs. Murillo, really knew much about music theory. If they did, they did not teach it to me.

We were taught how to read music, how to hold our hands and fingers on the keyboard. We learned to make the connection between lines and notes on printed sheets of music to the black and white keys of the keyboard. And, for most of us, that was all we needed to know.

Many years later, I was sitting in on a music lesson of one of my grandchildren. I, who was responsible for getting them to their lessons, heard Mrs. Smith say,

"Now Aaron, let me hear you play a second... now a third." At first amazed, I was thrilled beyond words to see that even beginning students nowadays were being taught music theory as a natural part of their keyboard training.

Much to my distress, none of my grandchildren, Terrence, Aaron, Cameron and Sarah, ever learned how to play the piano, but at least each of them had received a small amount of music theory training. My great-grandson, Evan, took up the violin as his instrument of choice in middle school.

The October when I was eight, Miss Burgess put me on the program of a music recital which turned out to be a contest, though neither my parents nor I knew that beforehand. All we knew was that I was to play something called *Chromatic Song.*

The recital was on a Tuesday evening—a school evening for my father, my sister and me. We thought it odd that the program would be on a weeknight, but it was and we went, taking the bus to the First Baptist Church.

My mother was wearing a black wool dress that had a white collar and carved ivory buttons down the front. She wore a stylish black cloche, and she had her usual black leather gloves. My father was still wearing the suit, blue shirt and blue tie he had worn to school that day. My sister had on a brown, pleated skirt and tan blouse with a brown sweater, and I was wearing a shiny dark blue taffeta dress and black patent leather shoes.

My family sat together in a row that was several rows behind the contestants who all sat on the front row. And even though several of her students were playing, Miss Burgess was one of the judges. She sat with the other judges at the front of the church. And so the evening began.

One after the other, each student played the piece they had practiced and memorized. When my turn came, I went to the piano, bowed to the audience, sat on the bench, adjusted my skirt, took a breath and ran my fingers up and down the keyboard fast, accurately and, even if I do say so, with nice phrasing. There was applause. I took another bow and returned to the front row with all of the other students.

After all of the students had performed, the judges went off to confer. Thirty minutes later, they returned. The teacher in charge, Miss Ward, came to the front of the room and said, "We want to thank all of you parents for allowing your child to play tonight. We know that music lessons cost money and that you have to make your child practice," here she smiled, "but we know that you know that these lessons are a gift to them. So, congratulations to you."

"And now for the winners." She paused. "Third prize goes to Pauline Estelle Merry." I pointed my finger to myself saying, *me?* Miss Ward said, "Yes you, Pauline Estelle. Please come forward."

I was so surprised! I looked out to the audience, toward my mother who was mouthing the words to me: *I thank you.* So I said, "I thank you." Miss Ward handed me a certificate with a blue ribbon on it. Then the second prize winner, a boy, Forrest Elliot, got a certificate with a red ribbon on his. The first prize winner's certificate had a gold ribbon on it. It, too, went to a boy, Harry Blackison.

My parents were in shock. They asked Miss Burgess why I had won. She said, "The piece, while it was fairly simple, required a dexterity that Pauline Estelle demonstrated with great skill." They both looked down at me, a bit perplexed; then they smiled and hugged me. I had unexpectedly won a prize. Now the evening was over, and the four of us went home.

After that evening, my mother and I began going to all kinds of classical music events.

Even though St. Louis was a segregated city, strangely, it allowed Blacks to go to any of the municipally-owned venues. In these, we could sit anywhere, if we had the money to buy a seat. In other words, we did not have to sit in the balcony, like we would if we went to any privately-owned theater. For example, the big Fox Theater wouldn't allow us to attend their shows, but the Kiel Auditorium did. The American Theater required us to sit in the balcony; the Municipal Opera did not.

It wasn't only the entertainment facilities. All kinds of places—schools, churches, movie houses, and of course housing were either for Blacks only or for whites only. These laws and traditions ruled everyone's lives —Black *and* white.

Let me share two examples which demonstrate the restrictions that diminished my life and, similarly, the lives of all Blacks living almost anywhere in the United States.

The first example shows how the city allowed use of a city-owned facility in Forest Park, but only sort-of. I have said that Blacks could use municipally-owned facilities. However, in this instance, not completely.

The showers seemed to be off limits. Once, my father and his friends went to play golf and then shower at the golf course. They were told that the showers were not available, but that they would be the next week. My father and his friends showed up the next week to play, only to be told that there had been a mix-up and the showers were under repair. Hmmm...interesting coincidence. I heard my father bitterly comment that the timing of the repair of the showers was no accident.

The other example was about pride versus permission. I remember one time my father was talking with one of his teacher colleagues, Mr. Roberts, about seeing *The Voice of the Turtle*, a play that had opened at the American Theater. These two highly-educated men were debating if they would swallow their pride and get tickets to see it there, knowing they would have to sit in the balcony. Even as a child, I wondered about the unfairness of their not being allowed to sit where they wanted. What did the owners think that they might do—throw watermelon rinds on the floor, or eat fried chicken and throw the bones at the other members of the audience? My father and Mr. Roberts decided not to go.

My mother decided that she and I would only attend events in facilities where we could sit where we wanted, thus some of our early forays together were attending the St. Louis Symphony Orchestra (SLSO) concerts at Kiel Auditorium. The SLSO was the second-oldest symphony orchestra in the country. It was there I first heard classical symphonic music—all kinds of symphonies by the great composers, Beethoven, Bach, Brahms and the like. I knew that I was hearing important music and I was happy to. Their works would set the foundation of my love for classical music.

My mother and I regularly sat in the balcony where the seats were cheapest. We were usually the only Negroes in the audience, but we were not the least bit uncomfortable with that. And I confess, I rather enjoyed being the only little colored girl in the audience. It set me apart, it made me feel special. I knew somehow that my mother and I garnered the approval of the white people in the audience. It was not that we were there to get it, but our assimilation into the larger, more powerful white world was considered to be the answer to better race relations and our being there, no doubt supported that assertion.

On the other hand, because my parents exposed my sister and me to sophisticated cultural events, we were often teased by our friends saying, "You are an Oreo: black on the outside, white on the inside." It was a criticism that I couldn't deny. Other friends of mine have confessed to also being called Oreos.

My relationship with my mother was very special. I tried to understand her as best a child can understand a parent. I did not like the idea that she didn't have many friends. She seldom ventured out. As I grew older, it fell to me to do the grocery shopping. And while she had an excellent eye for furniture placement, colors and design, she thought that her house was not good enough to have guests over.

Except for my father's teacher friends who would drop by occasionally, we never had anyone over to share a meal, have dessert, or just visit. The only exception was when, as we sat on the front lawn in the summer time watering the grass, she would easily mingle with our neighbors.

One day, my father was asked if my mother would like to be a member of Jack and Jill, an African American mother's group whose members tended to be mid- to upper-class, light-skinned African Americans. They were wives of doctors, dentists, lawyers, teachers—an elite, well-educated group of people. My mother would not join because, in addition to being very shy, she thought that our house would not meet the "what will others think" standards.

These are standards I now understand because, when I moved into a beautiful house as an adult, I said to myself, "Now I have a Jack and Jill house." And when I became a Jack and Jill mom for my oldest grandsons, I felt at ease having J&J meetings in my home. My sister wanted us to be in the St. Louis Chapter of J&J, and I don't think she ever forgave my mother for not being a Jack and Jill mom.

When my mother was offered a job at Homer G. Phillips Hospital to be one of its dietitians, I remember hearing my father say, "No wife of mine is going to work!" I hated that. I wanted to say to him, "We don't need her home every day. Let her take the job." But of course I didn't say that, and I am sorry that she didn't take it. I thought she would have had a much richer, happier, and more satisfying life if she'd had a job. But then again, I was just a child and any comments I would have made like that would not have gone over well at all.

My mother wanted me to excel, and I basked in her love and attention. I knew that she thought I was smart and talented and, quite probably, she saw me as becoming a successful adult. I remember hearing her say over and over: "You must be able to rely on yourself. Do not depend on needing a man to support you." These words were from a college graduate herself, whose husband did not allow her to work.

My mother took advantage of opportunities that would allow colored people to participate in public activities without embarrassment. That's why we also went to see the Metropolitan Opera when it came to St. Louis.

"You went where?" a friend said.

"I went to the opera with my mother."

"An opera?" she asked.

I laughed at her and said, "You don't even know what an opera is!"

The Metropolitan Opera's company of singers and musicians went on a six-week tour of several American cities following each of its seasons in New York. St. Louis was one of those cities. These annual spring tours brought the company and its stars to cities throughout the United States, because most of them had no opera company of their own.

The Met's national tours continued until 1986, but now we can see them almost anytime and anywhere on streaming sites. For me, seeing them on screen is almost as thrilling as seeing them in person. When I am asked today how it happened that I came to love opera, without hesitation, I tell about the times I went

*to the opera as a child with my mother, when the Met
came to St. Louis.*

Mother and I did not go every time they came to St.
Louis, but I vividly recall seeing and hearing *La Traviata,
Carmen, La Bohème,* and *Madam Butterfly.*

On the occasion before going to see *Madam Butterfly,* I
was standing in our living room between my father and
another teacher, Miss Frazier, while they discussed the
appropriateness of my seeing this opera.

*They thought that Cio-Cio-san was a prostitute.
Cio-Cio-san was not a prostitute. Pinkerton had in fact
married her, but then dumped her when he returned
to the United States and married a white woman.
Pinkerton was the scoundrel—not she. This is an
example too often repeated, where women are placed
in uncompromising situations, then blamed for
misbehaving—or worse.*

*My father's concern about what I might learn at the
opera went completely over my head. He needn't have
worried one bit—Puccini's music held me in its thrall,
the story, not so much.*

*I was thrilled with the stories and the singing of
grand opera was wonderful but, like many institutions
in the United States, racial equality for singers was
very slow in coming. By the time I was in college,
Rudolf Bing, who was the Met's leader for many years,
decided to open the roster to Black singers. Marian
Anderson's 1955 debut was followed by the
introduction of many a gifted and talented artist of
African American descent led by Leontyne Price. She
inaugurated the new house at Lincoln Center. Reri
Grist, Grace Bumbry, Shirley Verrett, Martina Arroyo,
George Shirley, and Robert McFerrin, were some of
the noted early Black singers.*

As my mother and I went to various concerts, I treasured
the time she and I spent together. As I learned more about
her life, I also learned of her dreams for me.

I went to Sumner High School with Grace Bumbry. In our 1954 year book, beside our photo and names were the careers we hoped to pursue. Beside her picture was 'Concert Singer.' Beside mine was 'Nurse.' I remember feeling full of pride when I saw her performance as Deliah on the Met's stage years later.

From the 1954 "Maroon and White" yearbook

Pauline Estelle Merry   Grace Bumbry
(Nurse)   (Concert Singer)

My mother was a brilliant woman. Her intelligence was often revealed in her clear and unusual perceptions and understanding of how the world worked. She did not just repeat things she read or heard about on the radio; she had her own interpretation of the meaning of events. She would comment about some piece of news and later I would hear that her opinions were right on. One example: After hearing a Marion Anderson concert, my mother said to me: "The accompanist played too loudly." Sure enough, the next day, in the *St. Louis Post Dispatch*, the concert reviewer said "Miss Anderson's accompanist played much too loudly, so loudly that Miss Anderson on occasion couldn't be heard clearly." Mother had been right.

On one of our outings to Kiel Auditorium, we went to hear, not the St. Louis Symphony Orchestra, but a talk by Adlai Stevenson. Of course we were nicely dressed. I wore a plaid skirt, white blouse, blue sweater and saddle shoes; my mother wore a blue navy wool, short-sleeved dress. Our hair was pressed and curled. It was in the early fall and she had taken along a navy sweater, in case the auditorium was chilly.

I did not get much of what Mr. Stevenson was talking about, although his opinions seemed to be changing the direction of the Democratic Party at that time, according to my mother. He was running for president of the United States for the second time and for some reason, my mother wanted to see him in person. In addition to being a pretty woman, my mother was also very smart, and seeing Stevenson helped her understand what he was offering to the country. I am still impressed with her intellect and her ability to express her ideas. My father was considered to be the smart one of the family, but I know that my mother was not "standing behind the door when brains were passed out."

There was always a book or two nearby that my mother was in the middle of reading. It was she who took my sister Freddie and me to the downtown main Public Library, and got each of us our own card. We could get cards, something which at that time would have been an impossibility for colored people in many other parts of the country. In fact, some places colored people couldn't even enter the library. As a result of my mother's intent to have us have our own cards, not only did I have a card, but I depended on books to make my life easier, brighter, and more understandable. Reading and a love of words was, in a way, my secret weapon against loneliness, ignorance, and boredom.

At a Sumner High School reunion, many years after we graduated, I caught up with my friend Dorothy Beckwith. She recalled that I told her to get a library card. She told me that not only did she get one, but she got her brother and sister to get library cards as well. And she thanked me for what I had done, and told me that my suggestion had directly lead to all of their subsequent professional successes.

Dorothy became a social worker. Her sister, Peggy, became a Doctor of Osteopathy, and her brother, Lynn, became an educator, teaching in St. Louis schools, rising to be a principal and later on a distinguished professor of Education at University of Missouri at St. Louis. Furthermore, he also became the president of the Board of Trustees for the St. Louis Public Library System.

All that, it seems, came from my telling her to get a library card! (No wonder, at one point in our history, a slave's ability to read could be punishable by death.)

My mother had lighter skin color than me and my sister, and she had dimples. She was the baby of a family that, interestingly enough, chose to educate its three girls and not the two boys. Irene was a teacher, Carrie Bell, a nurse. My mother's degree from Pratt Institute was in Home Economics, and she had worked in New York as a dietitian at Harlem Hospital, but she never worked again after she married my father.

What were her dreams, beside those of having her daughters do well in life? She didn't want us to follow her in her footsteps and simply be a housewife. I believe that she wanted us to make sure that we could take care of ourselves, and not rely on a man to provide for us. I heard her say this on more than one occasion. She was adamant that we be self-sufficient women, which of course meant that we would get to college. Never once did the words "When you get married, you won't have to work." cross her lips. Not once. Thank goodness.

Besides going to the St. Louis Symphony Orchestra performances, the Municipal Opera and lectures, if there were special artists who she thought I should see, I went. One was Philippa Duke Schuyler, a child prodigy pianist, composer, and later journalist. She was born August 2, 1931, grew up in Harlem, and was the only child of George S. Schuyler, a prominent black journalist, and Josephine Cogdell, a white Texan from a wealthy and socially prominent family. Her parents were not Harlem civil rights crusaders, but were conservatives and members of the John Birch Society. The elder Schuylers believed that interracial marriage and the resulting children could solve America's race issue. They fed Phillippa a strict raw food diet, believing that cooking removed all of the vital nutrients from food. Playing Mozart at the age of four and scoring 185 on an IQ test at the age of five, Phillippa quickly proved to her parents and the world that she was a child prodigy.

Years later I was saddened to learn of Miss Schuyler's tragic death in an airplane crash. She had left her life as a pianist and pursued a career in photo-journalism. She died on a photo shoot in Africa[2].

I saw her play the piano at Stowe Teacher's College. I went by myself to this concert, as the college was just down the street from my house in the quadrangle

Philippa Duke Schuyler & Stowe Teachers College

that was the center of educational and cultural life in The Ville. While I don't recall anything that stood out for me at the performance, not Miss Schuyler, what she wore, or what she played, I clearly remember walking into the auditorium and pausing at the top of the ramp and looking for a place to sit. This simple action of seeming to be in control of myself in the situation drew praise from Mrs. Brantley, the wife of the long time principal of Sumner. My mother beamed with pride as she related this to me. I was living up to her standards and those of the leading social arbiter of the St. Louis Black community.

---

[2] https://www.blackpast.org/african-american-history/schuyler-philippa-1931-1967/

My mother had started me on piano when I was five. I think she hoped that Miss Schuyler would be an inspiration to me, and that I might pursue a career in music. My final piano teacher, Mrs. Murillo, hoped that I might follow in the foot-steps of Hazel Scott. Neither artist inspired me to be a musician, but I did enjoy hearing them perform.

I think my mother envisioned me as a smaller version of Phillipa Duke Schyler, and so she came up with the idea that I would give piano recitals at small Black churches in and near Chestertown, MD when I went there to visit for the summer. She worked with my piano teacher and they came up with a list of pieces that I would practice, learn and perform in those small recitals. My Aunt Irene contacted the Black churches and arranged for me to give recitals on Sunday afternoons after the regular church services, or sometimes in the evenings after bible study classes. Most of them said, "Sure, Mrs. Graham, we would love to have your niece play for us. When is she coming and what do we need to do?"

I don't think that my mother thought that I would *be* a Phillipa Duke Schyler or anyone like that. She just thought that I played well and that I might bring an evening of classical music to the small rural Black communities. And so I did. I was Miss Irene's niece who was also proud of me and my playing ability. I had about eight pieces, among them a *Bach Two-Part Invention,* Chopin's *"Minute Waltz"*, *"Rustle of Spring," by Sinding,* and the well known Edward McDowell piece – *To a Wild Rose.* No jazz, no gospel, just European composers.

Generally the pianos were not quite in tune and were placed against a wall. I sat with my back to the audience which was often small, but people did come—I guess they came because they all knew Aunt Irene, and not to hear me. I loved doing these recitals. I was a little city girl "star" who was a bona fide musician. People would come up to me after I played and thanked me (me!) for playing for them. Many said that they wished they could play the piano. I just glowed as I stood near the small refreshment table, most often wearing a blue organdy short sleeved dress and I thanked them, with my pressed hair kinking up and me sweating because the churches were not air conditioned. But that didn't matter, not one bit. I had my mother, teachers, and aunt to thank for having these glorious occasions of playing music for an admiring audience.

In addition to my first piano teacher, Miss Burgess, I had two other teachers, Miss Ward and Mrs. Murillo. My transition to Miss Ward was fairly simple. Miss Burgess told me that I needed a better teacher than she was; she suggested that I move on to a teacher who could take me to another level.

Miss Ward was that teacher. She was Black and also lived in The Ville. Her many students included Harry Blackiston and Forrest Elliot, the two boys who had won first and second prize in the contest, where I had won third prize. She was a demanding teacher and required that we practice at least 30 minutes every day. Well, I loved practicing. My mother would sit by me most evenings after school when I did. She even enjoyed hearing my scales, but really liked better hearing me learn the pieces that I had been assigned. Those evenings were pleasant times for us both. And getting to my lessons at Miss Ward's house was no problem. I just walked from my house to her studio a few blocks away.

My next teacher was Mrs. Agnes Murillo. I don't remember how my mother found her for me, but getting to her place for those lessons was quite a different story. She was white and lived in Overland, Missouri, one of several cities that surround St. Louis. To get to my lessons with her, I had to take a bus from my house to the Delmar Loop station and then a trolley out to Overland. How I loved my Saturday morning trips out to her house. I went alone which allowed me time to think, to plan and dream, and to be on my own. I never felt afraid. I never felt unsafe. I never felt that I didn't belong.

Mrs. Murillo had a plan for me—and for her own professional growth. She presented me to her world as having "discovered" me, not admitting that I already had had half a dozen years of lessons before coming to her as a student. That seemed to work for us both. I was her little Black star. My mother said Mrs. Murillo must have thought she was the Sol Hurok (a famous impresario) of Overland, Missouri.

I did several recitals under her tutelage. At the last one I played a very difficult piece by Sergei Rachmaninoff, and I played it quite well. That recital marked the end of my piano performance career—except for a very tragic performance my first day of high school.

On that day, the principal of Sumner, Mr. Brantley, called on me in front of my new high school classmates and asked me to play. I had not been forewarned and therefore was not prepared. It was a miserable event from which both my father and I suffered—he being mocked by one of his fellow teachers at my less-than-stellar performance—and I became too afraid to play in front of others, ever again. I do not think that my father ever forgave me for embarrassing him that way.

It took years, but eventually I finally found the courage to perform music for others, once again. Mostly it wasn't by playing the piano—rather I played a harpsichord, and later a cello, both in groups and sometimes solo.

In addition to seeing and hearing famous instrumentalists performing classical music at the St. Louis Symphony Orchestra concerts, I also got to hear top quality musical theater at performances by the Municipal Opera at an outdoor amphitheater in Forest Park. This was yet another city owned/sponsored facility that Blacks could attend in that very racist city. We also had season tickets to it. Of course, there were no Black stars. My mother and I did see many classic musicals: *Of Thee I Sing, Desert Song, Oklahoma,* and many more. Being outside on hot summer evenings was perfect, and we sat anywhere we could afford. We would take the bus there, which dropped us in front of

the facility. We took the bus home, then walked along the darkened tree-lined streets to where we lived.

I loved my neighborhood. We lived not in a slum, but in a neighborhood that could boast of well-kept houses, green lawns, and precious trees. It was a middle-class neighborhood whose residents were a wonderful mixture of educated people, like my parents, and working class skilled laborers, like our next door neighbors, the Sloans.

Mr. Sloan worked at the steel mill and Mrs. Sloan had her own beauty parlor. Between them, along with their son John, they lived quite nicely, as did all our other neighbors. I dated the son of the only Black fireman in the city. He lived up the block from my house. It was a wonderful community. Public transportation was accessible and nearby markets sold fresh vegetables and fruit. Good schools were within walking distance. It was safe. I knew that I was very lucky to live where I did.

I recognized that the kinds of music I heard growing up were rich and varied: the hymns from the Episcopal Church Hymnal, the St. Louis Symphony Orchestra classical musical concerts, the Metropolitan Opera programs, light opera and musicals at the Municipal Opera, where I never saw or expected to see Black artists. And there were also all of the piano pieces I was assigned. I was lucky to see the great Marian Anderson, Roland Hayes and I even got to hear Paul Robson—all at Kiel Auditorium, but what was missing was the fabulous gospel singing that I heard only when I went to Chestertown, MD. The Episcopal Church I attended was not inclined to sing gospel music. Still, I loved the hymns we sang and their singular style often moved me when I heard them.

Jazz, that great African American musical invention, was not a part of my musical education. Except for spirituals and the occasional jazz piece, the only piece of music I knew to be written by a Black person was the music to "*Lift Every Voice and Sing*" by James Weldon Johnson. His brother, John Rosamond Johnson, wrote the lyrics. You may know this song as the Black National Anthem. Other than that piece, and some occasional Jazz, I rarely heard any music that I knew to be written by colored people.

But now, as with many things about African Americans that are coming to light, it turns out that, in addition to jazz (commonly acknowledged as a originally a Black art form), there is a lot of classical music that was written by a Black classical music composer. Until recently, William Grant Still is likely the only name of a Black classical composer that would come to most people's mind. A friend of mine, John Malveaux, hosts a web site called Music Untold[3]. On this site he presents classical music written by Black men and women—and he presents Black classical music—performers, composers, singers, and instrumentalists. John is determined that classical music written by Blacks be recognized in the classical music world as equal to that written by whites. I recommend visiting his website. The classical music world, which has had Black artists for a very long time, is now becoming more open and welcoming by

---

[3] https://musicuntold.com/index.php/musicuntold-projects/

acknowledging their existence and their extraordinary works of musical art.

Now, finally, I want to let you in on a secret part of my life (we are all full of secrets, you know). My secret is how I learned to love art and art museums, quite by chance.

One Saturday, after my piano lesson out in Overland, instead of coming directly home after I got off the bus on Kingshighway, I decided to go in the opposite direction from my house and visit Forest Park and explore its St. Louis Art Museum. I walked up a big hill and into the main building. Once in there, I wandered around the galleries for hours. I had no idea what I was looking at, not the artists, the styles, periods, what was good, what was great, what was mediocre. I knew nothing about the importance of the marble busts or the large colorful paintings. I just knew that they were things of wonder. It didn't hurt that the building itself was also beautiful. It was a large classical building, wide corridors, and rooms full of beautiful classical paintings.

St. Louis Art Museum
(statue of St. Louis and main entrance)

I had so much fun, I decided to do the same thing after many of my piano lessons.

The art museum overlooks a large green sloping lawn, the view from which allowed me to see more trees, other buildings and the small lake in the park. Green. Wonderful. Beautiful.

Lovely view of vast green lawn from the Art Museum

My visits were the beginning of my informal art education. Over time because of my visits there, my taste in art developed, and I found modern art more appealing to me than the older, "classical" art. Modern art seemed unlimited, challenging, and open. But no matter what kind of art I saw, I learned to appreciate the art world, just by being in the building.

Its spaciousness, beauty and all the paintings and busts filled me with joy, and my mind with wonder. Visiting the museum also felt mysterious—and even daring. I was often there by myself, alone in the galleries in the afternoon, the only colored person, and certainly the only little Black girl there. I felt challenged and adventuresome, and I felt my own sense of self expanding, just by being there on my own.

I thought about telling my parents about these visits, but I didn't. These visits were a private activity that I didn't want to share with anyone. I wonder, though, what they would have said, had I told them of my frequent art museum visits. Would they have said, *"Don't go there"* or *"Don't do that"*? On some level I regretted that I didn't tell them of these visits and how they affected me. I think that, had they known, they might have encouraged me to be an art history major, and I might have had a career in that immense field—so many possibilities. But I had not even heard of that as a career and, given their desire for me to have a good job, art history probably would not have occurred to them as a career path for me, either.

Another unrealized career I briefly thought about pursuing was to be a scientist. One day in the park, which is very near Washington University, I came upon a book sale. All sorts of books were randomly piled on tables, and I looked through a bunch and came across several books on science. They spoke to me and for a moment I pictured myself as a scientist in a white lab coat, intensely examining a test tube... and yet it was a very unlikely aspiration. Science, like art history, was a universe that I could only remotely consider as a place that I might visit, but hardly one where I could live.

So, I concluded that a career for me would have to be in something safe, like teaching. Or nursing, which would scratch the science itch a little.

As it turned out, teaching and nursing were the career options I chose and combined. In the process, I made a very successful professional life for myself.

A little aside here. My father regularly played chess with Arthur H. Compton, a Nobel Prize winning Physicist who was a professor at Washington University. My father had told me that Dr. Compton had stipulated that upon his death my father would be one of his pall bearers. However, when Dr. Compton died, his daughter didn't allow that to happen.

Seeing the greats with mother, my own explorations in downtown St. Louis, the St. Louis Art Museum, the main public library, the bookmobile, going to the Municipal Opera, Forest Park and other places—and being able to roam around North St. Louis and out to Overland on my own—woven through all of this, I somehow knew these activities would give me a life-long sense of my own strengths. I had an adventuresome spirit and I took advantage of opportunities that came along—or that I created—and I developed a sense of personal freedom that I intuitively knew would support me as I grew up.

Some Questions to Think About

1. What special place, like an auditorium or a theatre, have you gone to for a live performance? That 'special place' could also be in a church or outside in a park.

2. What special or 'famous' person, or group did you go to see? (Or, if you haven't done that, who would you *like* to see?) It could be a musician, an actor, a speaker, a group of performers, etc.

3. Have you ever seen a stage play with live actors, or a stage musical, or a live sports event in person (*not* on TV)? Who would you most like to go see 'live and in-person'?

4. What might keep you from going to see whomever you'd like to see? Might that be your age? The cost? The location? Or something else?

5. Have you ever gone somewhere away from home by yourself? How did that feel? How did coming home feel after that?

6. Do you play a musical instrument? If yes, what instrument? If no, what would you like to learn to play? Does anyone in your family play an instrument?

7. Have you ever performed on stage, in front of an audience? Have you ever put on a performance with friends, just for fun?

8. What do you think makes a person 'great'? Who is the 'greatest' person you have heard of?

9. Do you believe that you could be 'great' some day?

10. Imagine that! "Great!" Can you see yourself that way? Where will you be? How will you be dressed? What will you be doing? How will you feel?

If You Want to Learn More
Here are some good sources of information:

Marion Anderson, *My Lord, What a Morning*

https://www.goodreads.com/book/show/2261089.My_Lord_What_a_Morning

Shannon Potts, *Who Is Florence Price?* Written and illustrated by students of the Special Music School at Kaufman Music Center NYC, and their teacher. Schirmer Trade Books

https://www.cpr.org/search/?s=these-nyc-kids-have-%20written-the-history-of-an-overlooked-black-female-%20composer%2F

I'd love to hear from you, my readers.
You may contact me, the author, by emailing me at:
PaulineEstelleMerry@GreatTalesToldWell.com

Map: "My St. Louis"

Story 3
Where Have You Been?

Now I'm going to tell you about a very special adventure I had on a hot summer between fourth and fifth grade, in 1946. I solved a mystery!

* * * * *

I had just come home to our house on West St. Ferdinand one hot summer afternoon. I found my mother sitting at the kitchen table reading a book and drinking a tall glass of iced coffee. She glanced up and smiled at me. I smiled back.

4249 W. St. Ferdinand and Sumner HS in back

"Where have you been, Pauline Estelle?"

For some reason, I felt a little shy to tell her where I had been— even though she probably wouldn't have minded. So, I went ahead and said, "I was over at Tandy Park…just walking around."

"By yourself?"

"Mmm-hm."

"I thought so. Would you like a glass of milk?"

I nodded. She poured me some out of a glass bottle from the refrigerator. I sat by her, and we quietly drank together.

"What are you reading?"

"Richard Wright's *Native Son*."

We were alone in the house. I didn't know where my little sister Freddie was, but that wasn't unusual. We didn't spend much time together because of the difference in our ages. I

knew where my father was: he was teaching summer school
at one of the three high schools for Black kids.

We lived in what was called The Ville, an upper/middle-
class Black neighborhood in North St. Louis. It was the mid-
1940s and racial segregation was the way of life in the
United States and in most parts of the country. We were
called Negroes and lived separately from whites. We went to
segregated schools, and churches. We had our own hospitals.

The most important Black hospital was Homer G.
Phillips. It had a national reputation and was the place
where young doctors came from Meharry Medical College
and Howard University College of Medicine to do their
internships. It also had a nursing school, which is where I
went to train to be a Registered Nurse right after I
graduated from high school. People's Hospital was the other
hospital for coloreds in the city and, as it happened, that was
where I was born.

The local food stores, which were largely owned by Jewish
people, were in easy walking distance of my house. There
were churches of all different denominations, among them—
African Methodist Episcopal (AME), Baptist, Lutheran,
Holiness, Episcopalian, and Methodist. And in many ways it
was a perfect community where every necessary institution
existed: schools for kindergarten through college, hospitals,
churches, and markets selling plenty of foods.

In The Ville, there was a sense of community—a place
where everyone knew one another and where we kids didn't
dare misbehave because we knew that a neighbor would tell
our parents in a heart beat if we were caught being 'bad.'

I had just come back from my usual walk to the athletic
field nearby. The bookmobile was coming that afternoon, but
even with access to its promised treasures of new books, I
was mostly feeling restless. I wanted to do something, but I
couldn't figure out what that might be. I wanted an

adventure, anything to be exciting—or maybe even something naughty!

Of course, I didn't say this to my mother. She would have cautioned me to be good, not get into trouble, and certainly not do anything that might embarrass her—or, even worse, my father, who was well known in our community. What could a young girl do with those limitations and still have fun being adventurous?

Hmmm. What *could* I do?

There was the Mississippi River. Perhaps I could take the bus and trolley down to the riverside and go exploring along its banks. Maybe even hop aboard a boat and ride south along its path. (Clearly that was an impossible dream, but...someday, perhaps?) Or, I could take the bus and go out to Forest Park and see what I could find there. Or, take the bus which passed by our house, and go on a ride, just for the fun of it.

But none of these things really appealed to me—at least at that moment.

With nothing else to say to my mother, I left her reading and went upstairs to wait for the bookmobile. When it came, I went down and checked out three books. I started reading one until Mother called me to set the table for dinner.

But even with new books to read, for days I kept thinking, trying to figure out something *interesting* to do. I didn't have a friend I could talk to about doing anything really interesting, and my little sister was next to worthless for trying to talk to or do anything with.

Then that week, without warning, the opportunity for adventure showed itself to me in a very surprising way. I was reading in my room when I heard a loud knock on our front door. Now, my mother was a very shy person, and we didn't often have anyone come to our door.

It was Mrs. Nesby, who lived two doors down. Still, my mother answered cautiously. Mrs. Nesby rushed in, glancing over her shoulder. "Thank goodness you are here! I just had the strangest thing happen!" She was breathing fast.

My mother invited her to sit down and asked me to get her a drink of water.

I brought her the water. Mrs. Nesby sat down, gathered herself up and began to tell her story.

"A strange man came to my door asking for Mr. Nesby. I asked the man: 'Who are you? What do you want?'"

"What did he look like?"

"He was a young man, tall, slender, and his skin was chocolate brown. He was wearing clean navy wool pants and his green and yellow plaid shirt was open at the neck. Oh! He held a soft Black hat in his hands. No rings or anything."

"What did he have to say?"

"'Well,' he told me, 'I believe that your husband, Mr. Nesby, was a participant in the WPA Artists Project, and I would like to talk to him about what he learned about print making, and about some of his experiences in the WPA. I believe some of his work is quite interesting and could possibly be valuable and...' He paused for a moment."

The WPA, the Works Projects Administration, was a collection of government agencies set up to provide jobs for people during the Great Depression in the 1930s.

At that point, Mrs. Nesby, fanning herself with her handkerchief, went on to say that she was quite interested in what the man had to say because, even though she and Mr. Nesby had been married for many years, he had said very little about his life before they met and married. So, Mrs. Nesby asked the man to tell her more.

"But instead of answering me, he jumped up and said he had to leave, but he'd come back to tell us why he had sought out Mr. Nesby. Then that man turned and ran right out of my front door!"

That's when Mrs. Nesby came over to our house with this surprising event fresh in her mind.

At this point, I wanted to know more, so I invited myself into the conversation. I came over and sat down next to Mrs. Nesby on the couch.

"Do you think the man saw something in your house that surprised him, maybe that's why he ran out. Or, maybe he remembered something that he had to do and couldn't stay to finish his story." Or, I wondered, was he even who and what he said he was, someone who knew something about Mr. Nesby's past?

I asked Mrs. Nesby to try and remember everything about this young man, and if he had by any chance said anything more. I was thinking to myself that with more information, I would be able to find him and find out what more he wanted to say.

What I didn't say to her was that I was going to try and find him. No need to get her or my mother worried or, more importantly, have them tell me not to try and find him. This was going to be *my* adventure, the answer to my wanting to do something useful, interesting, and possibly even fun!

I politely asked again, "Mrs. Nesby, do you remember anything else about the young man? Did he say where he was staying? Did he say where he was going when he left so fast?"

Mrs. Nesby just shook her head, but then she added: "Oh, half under his breath, he did say that there was an older woman who lived in the basement of a house nearby, and that he was going to visit her also."

Hoping that he had, I asked, "Did he say her name?"

Mrs. Nesby frowned, paused, then said, "I think he said Miss Rose Thornton, but I'm not too sure."

"Anything else?" I asked.

"No, I don't think so. I was just so startled when he jumped up and ran out so fast—he didn't even get to talk to Mr. Nesby!"

Mrs. Nesby apologized to my mother saying that she was sorry to have disturbed us.

My mother said, "It is just fine. If there is anything that I can do, please come back and talk to me."

Mrs. Nesby said. "Thank you. If I need your help, I'll call you." She then went to the door and they said their good-byes.

My mother, smiled a little, looked at me and said, "Well, Pauline Estelle, that was interesting. What do you think that it is all about?"

I shrugged my shoulders and shook my head, trying to give her the impression that I had no interest at all in what had just happened, but my brain was working real hard! I wanted to solve this mystery: who the young man was, what his relationship to Mr. Nesby was, who was Miss Rose Thornton, and where did she fit in with all of this?

I said, "I don't know what it's about, but it is kind of mysterious, isn't it?" Mother agreed. Without saying any more to her, I excused myself and went to the room I shared with Freddie.

I sat on my bed to think. Maybe here was something I could do. I could find out who the fellow was, and what he wanted to talk to Mr. Nesby about. But how? How would I go about discovering the answers to this mystery that had just dropped into my lap?

I reasoned several things:

> **One:** The Ville is a small place where everyone knows everyone else, so any new person showing up would draw somebody's attention.

Two: I am smart. And I can find my way around the bus and trolley system. For example, my piano lessons in Overland, a city just outside the city limits of St. Louis, require that I take both a bus and a trolley to get there and takes over an hour each way.

Three: I already have some clues: the description of the young man, and what he said to Mrs. Nesby. And there is the mystery woman, who might be called Miss Rose Thornton, who lives in the basement of a house near ours.

Four: I have a library card to the city library. So if I need to, I can go to the library and get books out on any topic that might help, and I can also ask the librarian for her help.

Having a library card is special because in some southern towns, my mother told me, Negroes can't go to the library, let alone have a card that allows them to take books out. In St. Louis we can. And I'm so glad for that!

I rustled through a stack of books and papers and found a new, small, ruled notebook that was under the pile of other notebooks, and books and other stuff. I don't remember how I got the notebook, or why I hadn't written in it, but it was perfect for what I was now calling *The Mr. Nesby Case.*

That sounded kinda lame to me, but I figured that I could change the name later when I got more information. I started by listing all of the people who were a part of the mystery: Mr. Nesby, Mrs. Nesby, The Young Man, and Miss Rose Thornton.

I only realized that I had fallen asleep when my mother called me to come set the table for dinner. My father had already arrived home and my little sister was back from playing at Tandy Park with her friends all afternoon. Clearly, I would have to get back to my notebook later.

When we sat down to dinner, my father said grace, then turned on the radio to hear the St. Louis Cardinals baseball game, while we all ate.

My mother was a good cook and always seemed to be able to make tasty meals. She had been a dietitian before she married my father, and I guess her knowledge of food helped her be a good cook. There was little conversation at the table because my father demanded quiet so that he could hear Harry Caray announce the game. Even though Jackie Robinson had became the first Negro player in the major leagues and the St. Louis Cardinals had yet to sign up a Negro player, my father was still a Cardinals fan. So we listened to the calls that Harry Caray made. I learned more from his calls about baseball than I thought I would ever need to know.

My youngest grandson wants to play college baseball. Talking with him I have realized how much I learned about that game and its special language from those games I heard as a child. You never know when something you learn, even things you don't know you are learning, will turn out to be useful!

While we were eating, I was lost in thought about my new adventure. After doing the dishes and after the game was over, I would ask my father if he knew Miss Rose Thornton. I could barely contain myself from waiting to ask him about her. My father knew a lot of people in the community because of his work as a teacher and other community activities. I bet that he would have heard of her, even if he didn't know her.

It was a hot summer evening. After dinner, Freddie and I washed the dishes together, then we all got the lawn chairs and sat outside. My father watered the grass while my sister, mother and I talked. Our neighbors, Mrs. Prince and her twin daughters (whose birthday was the same as mine) and others, joined us.

I really enjoyed these hot summer evenings. We kids played hide-and-seek and caught fireflies in jelly jars. No arguing or fighting amongst us, just quiet, safe evenings in on a quiet safe street. We had many of those.

After a while, my father got tired of watering and sat in a chair next to my mother. They were quietly talking and I went over and sat next to him on the grass. Then tugging on his pant leg, I got his attention.

"Yes, Pauline Estelle, what do you want?" My father, who had been raised in Boston by his mother and older sister, had a lovely Boston accent. I loved to hear him talk.

I asked, "Daddy, do you know Miss Rose Thornton?"

"Who did you say?"

"Miss Rose Thornton," I repeated quietly.

He was quiet for a moment, thinking, then asked, "Why yes, I do. Why do you ask?"

It seemed like my mother had not told him about Mrs. Nesby's visit earlier in the day, so I said, "Ask mother about Mrs. Nesby's visit this morning."

He turned to her and said, "Pleen (as my father called her), Pauline Estelle said that Mrs. Nesby came over to our house today. Why?"

My mother answered, "Oh my goodness, I forgot to tell you. I can't image why I didn't, as it was so unusual. What did Pauline Estelle tell you?"

He said "That it was unusual and that I should ask you. So?"

"Indeed it was!" my mother said, and then she told him what had transpired (I had just learned that word— transpired. I like using new words.) I noticed with surprise that my mother didn't seem as distressed as I thought she would have been. While Mrs. Nesby was telling her what had gone on, it seemed to me that my mother had felt uneasy. Perhaps that was because people seldom came to our door.

After she finished telling my father about Mrs. Nesby's visit she looked to me and asked if I had anything to add. The only thing I had to add was the name: Miss Rose Thornton.

My father said, "Hmm, quite interesting."

Then he said to my mother, "What did the young man look like? She described him and my father repeated, "Quite interesting."

"Fritz (as my mother called him), what do you think about the young man's surprise visit to see Mr. Nesby? Does his behavior and his mention of Miss Rose Thornton seem odd to you?" Mother asked him.

"Pleen, I don't know what to make of the young man's visit. We will have to just wait and see what happens next. One thing I do know is that I do know Miss Rose Thornton and I would like to take Pauline Estelle to visit her sometime. She has a very interesting background and Pauline Estelle might like to know her."

I asked myself, "Why would I like to know her? I already knew a lot of people. Why her in particular?" In any case, she was connected to the mystery man and that was good enough for me.

But there was something else.

Sometimes I didn't quite understand my parents. The mention of Miss Rose Thornton caused me to think about them as two people. They seemed to love each other, and they took good care of my sister and me. But I am not sure they enjoyed each other. I felt a tension between them that made me feel uncomfortable.

But really, what can a child do about her parents' relationship? Not much. So, I learned to handle my emotions in a way that caused the least amount of fear for me, or anger from them. I think that, in some way, the nature of their relationship helped me to be very independent. I learned that I did not have to rely on them to make me feel okay about myself.

After talking about Miss Thornton, Daddy put the water hose away, while the rest of us picked up the lawn chairs. We all said good night to our neighbors and went in for the night.

Oh, and before we did, I opened my mason jar and let the fireflies out.

The next morning my new adventure jumped on me as soon as I woke up. I reviewed what I had written in my notebook. These notes included Mrs. Nesby's visit and her telling my mother and me what had happened. I had also written Mrs. Nesby's description of the young man and I remembered that Mrs. Nesby said something about a Miss Rose Thornton that the young man was going to visit.

After reviewing all I had written the day before, I drew a long line from the top of the page to the bottom, forming two columns. The heading for the first column was...what? I couldn't figure out yet then what the columns were to show, so I decided to come back to naming them later. I carefully secreted the notebook in the pile like it had been before. I didn't want anyone (like my sister) to think it was special and read it. Kinda like Edgar Allen Poe's *The Purloined Letter*, hiding in plain view.

At this point, I had no idea of how to find the young man, but it was important to me that I do so. I decided to give him a name and settled on Mr. Mystery Man. I felt certain that I would find him.

I thought it curious that my father seemed to completely ignore Mr. Mystery Man. Was there something that my father knew about him and wasn't telling me? But how could that be? He wasn't even there to see or hear the young man. I thought it interesting that he didn't seem at all curious about him. Yet my father had responded to the revelation that the young man had a connection with Miss Rose Thornton. Why was that?

I helped my mother clean up after breakfast. I didn't know where Freddie was or what she was doing, but as usual, she was nowhere to be seen when it came to doing chores. Oh well, I thought, it's just as well she's not around to get on my nerves or get in my way.

After breakfast, and after I finished my chores, I left the house. It was going to be another hot, muggy day, which meant that I could do pretty much whatever I wanted to do, especially since I had helped clean up the breakfast table.

I was wearing white cotton shorts, white tennis shoes, white socks and a light blue cotton blouse tucked into my shorts. My hair, which wasn't long, had been pressed and it was braided. I didn't like how it looked, but I did the best I could with it. I wished I had soft curly hair (what we called having "good hair"), but mine was what is called nappy hair. I had asked my mother if I could just wash my hair and not get it pressed, but she wouldn't let me. She said that I would look funny with my nappy hair just sitting on top of my head like a black cotton ball.

But what my mother really meant was that ideas of beauty in the United States were based on whiteness. Straight hair, fair skin, and blue eyes were the beauty standard against which little brown-skinned girls like me were judged.

I remember my mother had me use a skin lightening cream called "Black and White" on my face to make it several shades lighter. The cream was unpleasant to use, but my mother thought that it might make me look better— light skin better than dark skin. In fact, my father did comment favorably on how my lightened skin looked. But to keep using it would be a tireless, useless, never-ending endeavor, and after a while I stopped applying it to the skin on my face.

As for my hair, it would be many years later before I chose to wear my hair un-pressed (which is what was then becoming known as "a natural"). Once I did that I was told by the white assistant-principal where I had just started teaching that it didn't look professional and that I would not be hired any place else because of it. That might have been true then, but thankfully, over time that has changed.

And while "a natural" became an acceptable hair style for Black women in the business and academic world later on, having "textured hair" (any hair that's not straight) would continue to be a source of concern, so much so that so-called Crown Laws were passed, first in several cities, then in several states, and soon, perhaps, a national Crown Act will be passed. These laws make it unlawful to fire or penalize a person if his or her hairstyle is judged to be unprofessional.

The morning following Mr. Mystery Man's visit, and after breakfast, I hollered to my mother that I was leaving and would be back for lunch. I walked down the street toward Kennerly and the AME church, where I was in the Brownie Troop that met in the fall.

Next to the church, was an apartment house where Mr. and Mrs. Fox lived. Mr. Fox taught math at Sumner High School, which was right in the block behind our house on Cottage Ave. While my family had dark brown skin, the Foxes were very light-skinned, but they were still Black. It seemed that Negroes came in all shades including white, brown, and Black skin. The common factor that linked us all was that, somewhere in our lineage, someone had been of African descent, and it just took one drop of blood to be considered Black.

I went up to the Fox's apartment, knocked on the door and waited. Shortly, Mrs. Fox opened the door. "Oh," she said. "It's you, Pauline Estelle. What can I do for you? Is your mother okay? Is something wrong?"

"No, Mrs. Fox, everything is alright. I just wondered if you know of a new young man in town."

"A new young man?"

I had decided to come directly to the point, because I knew that she had two boys who were older than I was. They were probably close to the age or just a bit younger than Mr. Mystery Man who came yesterday to see Mrs. Nesby.

"Yes, Mrs. Fox, I am trying to find out if John or Robert might know of this new fellow who has come to town." I went on to describe to her the man who had visited Mrs. Nesby the day before, but I didn't tell her about the conversation he'd had with her. I didn't want to reveal that part of the story yet. I just said that Mrs. Nesby would like to have the man visit her again, and I told her I would try and help find him.

"Oh, Pauline Estelle, that sounds like a nice thing to do. I am sure that Mrs. Nesby would appreciate it. Let me see if John or Robert are still here. They told me that they were going out to meet some friends." She called out to them and happily both were still at home and came to the door.

"Oh hi, Pauline Estelle," they said in unison. To their mother they said, "Mother, we are just about to leave. Did you want us to do something for you before we go?"

Mrs. Fox said, "Pauline Estelle was hoping that you might know of a young man who is new in town." She repeated most of the description I had given her of The Mystery Man.

They didn't say anything at first, but then Robert said slowly, "I might have seen him. Why do you ask?"

"Well," I said, "I told Mrs. Nesby that I would try and find him for her. You know that Mr. Nesby is kind of sick, and I don't think that she really wants to leave him alone at home. And since school is out and I don't have much to do..." I stopped talking because I was beginning to feel like I was not making much sense, and just plain talking too much. And besides, why would a kid like me even think that she could find this strange young man.

It turns out that neither Mrs. Fox nor her sons seemed to think it was strange that I would want to try to find the young man. I supposed they just thought I was helping Mrs. Nesby—which was true.

Then Robert spoke up, "Yesterday, over at the park a small crowd of people were gathered in front of Sumner High. I know most of them, so they didn't mind me standing on the edge of the crowd and listening to what was going on." Then Robert asked me, "What did you say he looked like?"

So I described Mr. Mystery Man to them and Robert said, "Yes, that fits the description of the young fellow they were talking about. They were saying that he had come to town with some good news."

Good news about what? I was tempted to interrupt him and ask, but I wanted Robert to keep talking. Robert said that the young man, whom no one knew, had said that he had some good news and that he wanted to find the right people to tell it to. But then he took off in a hurry without telling them anything about what the news was or who needed to hear it. It was a repeat of what he had done with Mrs. Nesby.

Robert said. "The crowd of people, mostly teachers from the high school, had just dismissed him as some sort of lunatic who could be ignored.

"When the group broke up and went their different ways, as summer school was over for the day, I followed the young man and caught up with him. I asked him if I could help."

This surprised me. Robert seemed to me to be a very shy person. I didn't imagine he would get into a conversation with a stranger.

Robert went on, "The young man asked if I knew of an inexpensive place that he could stay as he didn't have any friends or relatives in the Ville. To which I suggested that he try the colored YMCA. I guess that that is where he went."

I didn't remember to ask Robert if he knew The Mystery Man's name, so that was still a mystery.

Now I had five elements to my mystery:

1. Mystery Man—Who was he?

2. What was his connection to Mr. Nesby?

3. Miss Rose Thornton—who and where was she?

4. Good News—What is it?

5. Did he go to the YMCA?

It was still mid-morning and, as I had told my mother that morning that I would be home for lunch, I had to go home now, but maybe I would have time after lunch to find out more about Mystery Man. I said thanks to Robert and John and good-bye to Mrs. Fox and walked back toward my house, past the church, turned left on Kennerly, and headed toward Tandy Park.

Sumner High School faced the large athletic field with the tennis courts on its west end and the Tandy Recreation facility on the east end. Stowe Teacher's College was across the street from the tennis courts and on the north side of the rectangle was the Turner School for handicapped children.

On the east side of this rectangle was the Annie Malone Orphan's home. In all the time I lived in The Ville I never went into the orphan's home, but I was always curious about what it looked like inside. I didn't know any child who lived there, but then again, kids wouldn't walk around with a sign around their necks saying that that is where they lived, any more than I wore something around my neck saying where I lived.

In the meantime, I thought that if I went over to the tennis courts near where my mystery man had held forth with the small crowd, I might learn more about him. After lunch I planned to head over to the Y, but for now, I'd just casually see what I could learn by sitting and watching tennis being played and listening to any conversations that might be going on.

I was alone on the bleachers. I watched Mr. Hudlin coach some tennis players.

He became quite well known later as having been one of Arthur Ash's coaches, but that morning there was just him and a few of his local students.

I didn't give them much attention because I was puzzling about what kind of 'good news' the mystery man might have been talking about, and why had he announced it in front of strangers? What was the connection, if any, between the 'good news' and Mr. Nesby and Miss Thornton? I was beginning to think that I should first find the mystery man and ask him these questions myself. Then, I would tell Mrs. Nesby. Soon, it was almost time for lunch. I went home feeling that I had at least the beginnings of a plan of action.

When I got home, I went straight to my room. I wrote the names of these characters and some unclear ideas on a line next to the left margin. I still didn't have headings for the columns, but I knew those would come to me as I got new information.

Sitting at the kitchen table, I found my usually-somewhere-else little sister Freddie, and a friend she had invited home for lunch. Lunch was jelly sandwiches, some orange slices, some potato salad and milk. It was tasty.

Soon I was ready to leave on my secret errand to the Y. I said good-bye to my mother and left my sister to clean up the table with her friend.

I decided to catch the bus to go to the Y. I had enough money from my small allowance to be able to take the bus. The Y for Negro men was near one of the big Baptist churches. I went into the building. Behind the front desk sat an older, grey-haired man.

I said, "Good afternoon, sir."

"What can I do for you, miss?"

"I'm looking for a young man who came to visit my neighbor down the street from me and I learned today that he might be staying here. I need to talk to him."

"What is his name?"

"I don't know," I replied, "but I can describe him to you."

After I said that, the man behind the desk said, "Oh, I know who you are talking about, but I don't think he is here —wait, yes he is, his key is not in the box. That means he has it and is in his room."

I got really excited about this information and I asked, "Can I go up to his room and talk to him?"

The man said, "No, of course you can't. But I can go knock on his door and tell him that he has a visitor. Will that be okay?"

"Oh, yes, sir. Thank you."

He got up from behind the desk and headed toward the stairs while I found a chair, sat down, and waited.

After what felt to me like a long time, he came back down and said, "The young man said that he would be down in a few minutes." I waited and waited and waited.

After a bit longer, I went back to the desk and asked the man. "Do you know why it is taking so long for the young man to come down."

He said. "I don't know. I will go back up to see what's happening." He came back down shortly, and said, "It seems that the young man is no longer in his room."

"What do you mean?" I asked.

"He didn't answer my knock."

With that information, I said thank you to the man and left. What was going on with the young man? I believed that the man at the desk wouldn't know, and there was no point in asking him any more questions. I then decided to walk back home. It would give me more time to think.

And then, to my surprise, I saw who I thought might be my mystery man. He was walking along the street in the same direction that I was going, as though he had a destination. I started to run to catch up with him, but then I decided to follow him, to see where he was going. I knew that he didn't know me, and so he would just think that I was just some girl going the same direction as he was.

We walked and walked. I felt safe because we were on Page Avenue, a very busy street with lots of cars, buses and people walking. Along the street, the houses were well-kept, many had stone fronts, and neat lawns. But looking at the scenery was not my objective. I was on a mission. Like in mysteries I had read or that I'd heard on the radio, I was secretly following someone. After a bit, he turned off the busy street onto a quieter one. I faced a quandary: I wanted to follow him, but I didn't want him to notice me. So I slowed down, but still keeping him in sight.

He made yet another turn and now we were on Lewis Place. He walked right up to 4709 Lewis Place, knocked on the door, and it was opened by an older, light-skinned woman with white hair. He greeted her and, after a bit of conversation that I couldn't hear, she let him in.

I decided to wait for him to come out. I knew that I couldn't just follow him up to the door. I had to figure out if I should I follow him after he left her house or go up to the door and talk to the lady. I thought, "Okay, Pauline Estelle, just wait, and then follow him back to the Y—if that was where he is going next. But in any event, I'll wait and try to talk to him."

After about half an hour, he came out. She was smiling and so was he. They said their good-byes at her door, and off he went—back toward the Y. This time I decided to catch up with him and introduce myself. I'd tell him what I knew and ask if he would tell me who he was and about Mr. Nesby.

I shouted at him, "Hello. Oh, hello, sir. May I walk with you? I want to talk to you for a bit."

He stopped and waited for me to catch up with him. He didn't smile, but he also didn't look mad. I started talking real fast.

"Hi! My name is Pauline Estelle and I want to help Mrs. Nesby. Someone said that you have good news, and I would like you to tell me who you are and,"—I had to catch my breath. "Oh, I want you to tell me about Miss Thornton and…."

"Whoa, little girl. You are talking too fast for me. Slow down and start over."

By now we were back on Page Avenue, walking back toward the colored Y.

I took a breath and said, "First, please tell me your name. I already told you that my name is Pauline Estelle."

He smiled down at me and said, "My name is Joseph Edwards. Pleased to meet you, Pauline Estelle." Well, finally I knew his name and no longer had to call him Mr. Mystery Man.

"Pleased to meet you too, Mr. Edwards." We then started to walk again toward the Y. I asked him the most important question I had. "Why did you rush out of Mrs. Nesby's house?"

He looked surprised at my question, and quite frankly, I was surprised myself to hear that this was the first question out of my mouth.

He slowed down a little and asked me how I knew that he had run out of Mrs. Nesby's house. "She told my mother, and I was listening to their conversation."

"Oh, so you are an eavesdropper as well as a follower?" He laughed and said, "Just kidding. I do need to go back and apologize to Mrs. Nesby for my behavior. I should have given her an explanation. I must have scared her. Did I?"

"Yes, you did! And me, and my mother too. Mrs. Nesby came to our house to tell us about your visit, and your abrupt exit. It was and still is a mystery to us all," I said this in a hurry, afraid that he might run off again. "And I also want to know about Miss Rose Thornton—and what the good news is."

Now, he really looked surprised.

"How do you know about the good news?"

"My friend Robert heard that you were talking in front of Sumner High School, and they said that you said that you had some good news."

"My goodness gracious, I really left a trail of mysteries, didn't I?"

"You really did! And I want to know the answers to those mysteries—and even more. Are you going to tell me the whole story?"

By this time we were almost back to the Y, and I knew I still had to find a way to keep in contact with him.

"Oh, and one more thing. You took your room key with you when you left the Y, and you had told the desk clerk you were going to come down to see me. Later the man at the desk found out that you had left. Why did you leave without talking to me, or leaving your key when you left the Y?"

With that question, he laughed out loud. "My goodness, you really are an inquisitive little girl! I was in such a hurry to go on my errand that I just forgot about to leaving my key when I left the building. I didn't mean to make the desk man angry or worried, and I totally forgot about you." Sigh. "Yet two more people I have to apologize to."

"Yes, you do have a lot of people to apologize to—or at least end their speculation (another new word of mine) about everything. Not knowing who you are and then you leaving quickly and all of those mysterious behaviors— that's made a lot of people curious, and some even concerned."

We were now at the Y entrance and, without thinking, I blurted out, "After dinner, my mother, father, little sister and I sit on our front lawn. Maybe you could come over this evening and meet them. And maybe Mrs. Nesby might join us, since she lives two doors down the street from us." He said that he would think about it and maybe he might. So I said good-bye to him and headed home.

As soon as I got to my house, I let my mother know that I was back, went to my room, pulled out my notebook, and started writing. I was beginning to feel a little better about the mystery man, but I wanted to put my thoughts down in an organized way.

I opened to my note page and looked at all of the names in the left column:

Mrs. Nesby

Mr. Nesby

Joseph Edwards (Mystery Man)

Miss Rose Thornton

Pleen (Mother)

Fritz (Father)

Mrs. Fox

Robert Fox

John Fox

My little sister, the desk man at the Y, the crowd in front of Sumner—these were, as I have learned to describe them, minor characters who, at least at the moment, played no key role in my story, but they still had to be accounted for.

As for the columns across the top of the page, I still had nothing to call them, so I left them blank. After writing all this down, I realized that I hadn't asked Joseph about Miss Rose Thornton. Oh well, I thought, perhaps he will tell us about her when he comes to our house. If he does.

Around 5 p.m., the four of us sat down for dinner. This evening there was no Cardinal baseball game; instead, we listened to a radio story, perhaps it was *Green Hornet* or *The Shadow*, I'm not sure. Again, my father wanted to hear the program and asked that we all be quiet. That was okay with me because I liked these programs. They were always stories that made the listener make up pictures of the characters and places in their own heads.

Right after dinner and the table had been cleared, we went out front like the night before. St. Louis was and is known for its hot, muggy summers. "It's not the heat, it's the humidity" was the common phrase exchanged as a greeting.

Again we got our lawn chairs, my father watered the grass, I played hide-and-seek with my sister and other kids in the block.

I agreed to be "it" for the first round.

> *"There's a bird in the tree, mus' I kill it? NO.*
> *There's a bird in the tree mus' I kill it? NO!*
> *Ready or not, you shall be caught*
> *in your hiding place or not!*
> *Here I come!"*

Then everyone ran to touch the tree before I could tag them. And I took off running to find the hiding kids. If they got to the tree without me tagging them, they were safe. If I tagged them, they were out and would be the next person who was it. We did this over and over until we all fell down, tired and laughing. We trapped more fire-flies in jars, and played hand-slapping games.

The neighbors joined us again as well. But this evening was different for me. I kept looking up and down the street for Mr. Edwards, but he never showed up.

About 9 p.m., we called it a night and went in the house, where every screened window was open to let in the cooler night air. I was really disappointed that Mr. Edwards didn't show up, but I wasn't going to let his not having come stop me from continuing my investigation.

The next morning, I got ready to leave the house after breakfast, telling my mother that I was going over to the park. This morning I wore blue shorts and a blue and white seersucker, sleeveless blouse. It was one of my favorite blouses and of course my white tennis shoes and white socks. My hair, as usual, was in short braids.

I'd had a busy day the day before. I wanted to be outside alone, to think about what I should do next. This time I took my notebook and sat on a bench near the tennis courts.

I looked over each and every name on my list. Nothing came to me, except the facts (1) that my father had not taken me to see Miss Thornton, (2) nor had he said when he would. I decided to ask him this evening when he would take me to see her. But my activity for the morning was what was really on my mind.

I had decided to take a walk over to Lewis Place and look at the house where I had seen Joseph enter. But before I did, I went back to my house and put my notebook back into its hiding place. I felt it was safer there than in my little 'stuff' bag. I yelled "I'm leaving!" to my mother as I left. She called back that I should be home for lunch around 1 p.m. or so. I said I would. Then off I went to Lewis Place.

It was a nice walk from my house to there, and not too warm for that time of day. Soon I saw the house that I'd seen Mr. Edwards go into. and I saw the same lady who had let him in the day before. She was out in the front yard, doing something with some plants in front of her picture window. She was wearing a short-sleeved dress with yellow flowers. It had a full skirt and she was wearing white Bernardo sandals. Should I go talk to her, or just walk by?

The house was on the other side of the street from where I was walking, so I crossed over to be on the side where she was. I slowed down a little and softly said, "Good morning, ma'am."

She looked up, smiling, and said, "Why hello there, young lady. How are you this morning? And do I know you? I don't remember seeing you before."

"I am fine thank you, ma'am and how are you? And no, I don't think we have met before."

The lady continued to smile at me as I stood on the sidewalk. I was trying to decide if I should mention Joseph's visit the day before. Finally I said, "My name is Pauline Estelle, and yesterday I walked by your house."

"Oh you did, did you? And why was that? Do you live nearby?"

"I don't live very far from here. But the reason I was here yesterday is that I followed a young man who visited you. I was following him because he…"

"Wait, wait a minute, Pauline Estelle. You are going too fast for me, so slow down and start over. And by the way, my name is Miss Thornton."

"You name is what?!" I almost shouted at her. "Miss Thornton? Miss Rose Thornton?"

"Yes, I am Miss Rose Thornton. Is there something wrong?"

Oh my goodness, oh my goodness! Wait! Now what? What was I to do now? So I said quietly, while breathing loud and fast, "Miss Thornton, may I please have a glass of water? And may I sit on your lawn for a little bit?"

"Are you all right?"

"Yes ma'am, but I sure could use a drink of water right now."

She said, "Don't move. Wait for me to return."

She came back with a glass of water for me and an aluminum lawn chair. She invited me to sit, and she went to get another chair.

My chair was one of those shiny, green metal ones with a seat that looked like a flattened flower petal to me. Anyway, I sat and she soon returned with her chair.

I drank almost all the water without stopping. I put the glass (actually it was greenish-colored aluminum tumbler) down on the grass, took a breath, and then the words of my story began to pour out. I said, "I learned from my neighbor, Mrs. Nesby, that a young man had visited her. He had said that he wanted to talk to Mr. Nesby about some work Mr. Nesby had done, but before Mrs. Nesby could respond, he had suddenly jumped up and ran out of the house without any explanation, except saying that he would be back.

"Mrs. Nesby told us her visitor also said that he was going to visit Miss Rose Thornton. After making some inquiries, I went to the colored Y where I thought he might be staying. I followed him yesterday, and he came to your house. And just now I discovered that you are Miss Rose Thornton. Oh, and one more thing, my father says that he knows you and that he is going to take me to visit you."

I think that I said all that in one breath!

Miss Thornton kept looking at me. Her face kept changing: from wonder, to smiling, to laughing out loud, to just quiet. I didn't know what to expect, but I was surprised that so many expressions crossed her face. In my experience with grown-ups, they hardly let their faces reveal what's on their minds, especially when talking to a kid. So then I stopped talking and waited for her say something.

Miss Thornton took a few moments before saying anything, and then she asked, "What is your father's name?" Well that was a surprise. The first thing she asked me was about my father and nothing about the visitor.

"My parents are… my parents are Frederick and Pauline Merry."

"Who?" she said, her voice rising in surprise, "Who?"

"My parents are Frederick and Pauline Merry," I repeated.

Well, at first Miss Thornton just sat in her chair and didn't say a thing. Then she seemed to gather herself, and said, "Well, what a small world! I haven't seen your father for a while, and here you are showing up at my house, without so much as a 'howdy-do' telling me this story. Well, actually your reason for being here is a little strange, but never-the-less, here you are. My goodness, gracious!"

By this time, I was calmer myself. She asked me if I wanted more water, and I said that I would like a little more. So she went and got me more to drink.

Then she said, "Okay, Pauline Estelle, let's get back to the young man who visited me yesterday. He told me that his name was Joseph…."

"Joseph Edwards," I prompted.

"Yes," she said slowly, "Joseph Edwards."

"If I may be so bold to ask, what did he say?"

Miss Thornton looked thoughtful, as though she were recalling what he had said to her. I remembered that he hadn't been inside her house for very long—about half an hour—so I figured that what he had said to her could not have been that important, or that complicated, but I was wrong.

Miss Thornton explained that Joseph had come to The Ville to find her and Mr. Nesby and to share some information he had for the two of them. He said that he wasn't ready to reveal what that information was right then, but that he would in the next several days.

Boy, this was becoming more and more mysterious, and I had even more to wonder about. What was the information and why was he behaving so mysteriously? I had recently heard someone say: "Sometimes we put a period at some point in life, when really that was a place for a comma." I wondered if this was a comma in both Mr. Nesby's life and Miss Thornton's life. And if something good and interesting was to come out of that place for the both of them now. And if Joseph Edwards would eventually explain what it was.

"Do you know Mr. and Mrs. Nesby?" I asked Miss Thornton.

She scrunched up her nice face in a thoughtful way and said, "I might. You say that they live down the street from you? What is the name of your street?" she asked.

"St. Ferdinand. We live on the street behind Sumner."

"Oh," she said. "I know exactly where that street is—up the street from Homer G. Phillips Hospital."

"Yes it is."

By now it was almost time for me to get back home, so I asked if I could come back that afternoon or the next day to talk some more. She said fine, she would be working in her yard the next day at about the same time that I had come today. With that, I thanked her again for the water and we both said good-bye.

Since I had no plans to stop anywhere else, I went on home. I called to my mother, letting her know that I was back. I went up to my room, pulled out my special notebook and stared at the one and only page that had anything on it —the list of names.

I decided that, so as not to get confused about who was who and how they fit into the story, one of the two columns I had yet to name would be the date I had talked to each of them. Then I would give each of the most important names a page on which I would write notes about conversations or activities—like having found and talked with Miss Rose Thornton.

With that plan, I wrote by each of the names the date that I had talked to them, as close as I could remember. Then I started a page for Mrs. Nesby, one for Joseph, and one for Miss Thornton. I wrote on each of their pages the key ideas about them that I didn't want to forget.

Having started that, I felt good. I felt like I was being orderly, conscientious and I even felt a bit proud of how I was organizing and managing this summer adventure—at least on paper.

After lunch, I walked down to Mrs. Nesby's house. I knocked on the door, which she quickly opened and invited me in. She was wearing a pretty greenish blue dress and what are called sensible, brown oxford shoes. Her hair was neatly arranged in an upsweep pompadour. I walked in and said hello to Mr. Nesby who was sitting wrapped in a light blanket—even though it was warm—in their sun room.

Mrs. Nesby asked quietly if I had anything to tell her. She invited me to sit with her on their back porch, and I told her all of the things that I had learned. I told her that I had found and talked with Miss Rose Thornton, who didn't live in a basement after all, but in a rather nice house on Lewis

Place. And saving the best for last, I told her that I had found the young man—with some help from Robert Fox.

Mrs. Nesby didn't say much of anything while I told her my progress, but she seemed quite impressed with all that I had learned, especially without my having had many clues at all to start with.

Mrs. Nesby asked me, "What do you think the connection with Miss Thornton and Mr. Nesby is about—any clues?"

"I'm not sure."

After a moment's thought, I said, "Well, it seems to me that it must have been something in their past, not anything recent, or you would know about it, but I think it must be a good connection. Joseph told the small crowd in front of Sumner that he was a bearer of good news, but that still makes little sense to me. Why would he say that to a crowd of strangers, like something a holy-roller preacher would say?"

Mrs. Nesby and I didn't say anything for a little bit. Then she said, "Why don't we talk to Mr. Nesby? He is, after all, who Joseph came to see."

So we did. We went out to the sun room, and I repeated to Mr. Nesby everything I had learned. It turned out that Mr. Nesby did know Miss Thornton. She had helped him with paperwork that he needed to complete in order to get into Lincoln University in Pennsylvania. It was an all-Black men's college at the time. He said that once he got enrolled, he lost contact with her and was surprised to learn that she was here in St. Louis.

Well, I suppose that happens. Mr. Nesby didn't seem much interested in trying to reconnect with her now, maybe because he's not well. But in any event, his connection with her seemed quite interesting to me, even though I didn't quite understand all that he said. So I asked him to tell me more about him and Miss Thornton. I noticed Mrs. Nesby leaning in to hear what he had to say.

He began, "While I was still in the army during WWI, I wrote to the Dean at Lincoln University about going there after I was discharged. My point of contact, it turned out, was Miss Thornton. After I got my degree in Painting and Art History, I couldn't find any work anywhere. I couldn't make a living as an artist, and I tried unsuccessfully to get teaching jobs in schools or in other Black colleges (this was around 1936). Somehow, Miss Thornton learned of my situation and came to my rescue again. She directed me to the WPA office, and there I got work as a print maker for the WPA in 1938, the peak of WPA activities."

Now I knew about Mr. Nesby and his connection to Miss Rose Thornton. But what about Joseph and Mr. Nesby, and Joseph and Miss Thornton?

"Thank you, Mr. Nesby, for telling me about how you came to know Miss Rose Thornton."

Mrs. Nesby said, "Thank you for telling us both about what you have learned so far."

I said, "I'll be back once I learn more. Would it be okay if I could please come and ask both of you more questions to help me solve my mystery?"

Both of them said, "Yes."

I said good-bye and went home.

In my room, I pulled out my hidden notebook and wrote down these questions:

1. What is Mr. Nesby's connection to Miss Rose Thornton? (I now know the answer to that one.)

2. What about Joseph and Mr. Nesby? (To be determined!)

3. What about Joseph and Miss Thornton? (To be determined!)

Even though I didn't know the answers to the second or third questions, I felt I was making some progress.

After lunch, I told my mother I was going to go downtown to the library. Although I didn't need an excuse, I said I was going to check out some books.

I had joined the Read-Away-Vacation Book Club and needed more books to read. The Club's goal was to encourage reading. This was accomplished by seeing how many books you could read during the summer vacation. For having participated in the club, a kid would get 'A Certificate of Participation.'

I could get books from the book-mobile that came to our neighborhood, or I could go to the downtown Public Library. Either would provide me with enough reading material to last me maybe two weeks. The difference was that the book-mobile came to our neighborhood. Otherwise, I had to go downtown to the library.

That summer I read 93 books. I told my friend, Frances that, and she said she had read 95.

My mother said that I shouldn't have told Frances how many books I had read because that caused Frances to try and read more than I did. I didn't know that I was competing with anyone, but it was an interesting lesson to learn. You don't have to tell your personal business to everyone.

I decided to take the bus and trolley downtown and go to the library to see what I could find out about the WPA. I was wearing a pair of blue shorts again, but this time I had on a light blue blouse and of course, my white tennis shoes. I decided to wear blue socks to match my blouse. I didn't need a sweater because it was another hot day. I thought that I should look nice if I was going downtown.

The St. Louis Public Library is in a large, beautiful building, near Kiel Auditorium and not far from Union Station. The trolley stopped right in front of the entrance. I went up the steps, into the building, and asked the librarian if there were some books about the WPA, and if so, where would I find them.

St. Louis Public Library
Main Entrance

I was not shy about asking for things that I wanted, even if I were asking a white person. Somehow, I had gotten it into my head that my skin color didn't matter, even though we lived in a segregated city. I just wasn't afraid. I somehow thought that because I was smart, it didn't matter what color I was. The stupid segregation restrictions were a nuisance, but in-and-of-themselves didn't reflect on my own personal value and strengths. I think that this was a special gift from my parents. And even if the librarian looked at me a bit strangely, it didn't make me want to apologize for asking. And if one smiled at me, I didn't see anything really special in that either, but perhaps it was.

The librarian told me where I would find some books on the topic. I thanked her, walked up the grand staircase, found the room she directed me to, and then I asked another librarian about the WPA. Here is some of what I learned.

The Works Project Administration (WPA) was a government agency set up during U. S. President Franklin Delano Roosevelt's first 100 days in office in 1933. It was needed, since after the 1929 crash of the stock market, and up until the start of WWII in 1941 a huge number of people weren't able to find work. The WPA was designed to give people work. It and some other government agencies provided a source of income, enough to let many people meet their basic needs. Mostly these were jobs in construction, building lots of streets and bridges and much housing. The WPA also employed artists, writers, and other sorts of creative people. These programs ended at the beginning of WWII because building air planes and weapons and other war related items provided much better jobs than the WPA.

More importantly, the WPA provided Black artists who otherwise would have starved with a way to explore and express their own creativity while making at least a modest income. One kind of creative work they supported was developing new printmaking processes all while earning at least a modest income. This was really a big deal for Blacks in particular, because this helped at least some Blacks to survive in their own native land—the place where we as a people are still not welcomed. I also learned that examples of prints made by Black artists supported by the WPA can be found in the Library of Congress.

So it seems that going to the library was a good idea. I certainly now had some interesting background information that would help me with my investigation.

Before I went home, I walked down the street from the library to see the large, mysterious sculpture, in front of Union Station. It has lots of water spouting, with naked male and female figures. I wondered about it, and on another trip to the library, I looked up why it was important.

I learned that the sculpture, called *Meeting of the Waters*, was a tribute to a rich lady's husband. She wanted to do something nice in his memory, so she hired a sculptor to build it. The meaning of the sculpture's name is that it celebrates the meeting of the Missouri and Mississippi Rivers at St. Louis.

I further learned that The Mississippi River is represented by the male figure, and the Missouri River is represented by a female figure. The water sprites, mermaids, and fish symbolize the seventeen main tributaries that enter the two rivers. It's made of bronze. To me it was daring and mysterious, beautiful, and it conjured up out-of-reach dreams in my mind. I loved it!

After I visited the library and made my side trip to see the sculpture, I returned home and again, after dinner my mother, father, sister and I sat outside on another hot summer evening. My father watered the grass as was his custom and we kids ran around collecting fireflies and playing hide-and-seek.

In the middle of one of the games, I was it. I went to the tree, put my head on its trunk, covered my eyes and started yelling:

> *"There's a bird in the tree, mus' I kill it? NO.*
> *There's a bird in the tree mus' I kill it? NO!*
> *Ready or not, you shall be caught*
> *in your hiding place or not!*
> *Here I come!"*

We laughed and hollered and ran and tried to tag each other. It is always such fun!

After a while, I told the kids that I wanted to rest a bit, and I went and sat by my father. Then, even though he was still watering, I said, "I met Miss Thornton." I don't know why it popped out of my mouth at that moment, but it did. My father looked at me in surprise, propped the hose he was holding on a rock, turned to me and said, "Well now, how did that happen?" He didn't seem angry.

"I followed Joseph."

"What? Who?"

"I found the man who visited the Nesby's, and I followed him to Miss Thornton's house, only I didn't know at the time that it was Miss Thornton's house."

Now, my father is a quiet, cautious man and in particular, he is concerned about my sister's and my safety. He told me he did not like the idea that I had followed some strange man to some strange lady's house, even though it turned out that my father knew her.

I explained to my father that I had told Miss Thornton who my parents were, and that she seemed pleased to have met me.

"She lives on Lewis Place and she invited me back to visit her again any time. I hope it's okay with you that I met her already."

Some of the houses on Lewis Place

"Of course I am happy that you met her. Now I really have an excuse to go see her. I am impressed that you found her on your own. It would seem that you are more adventurous than I thought. I just want you to be careful when you are out and about. You mean a lot to me, and I wouldn't want you to get hurt." He smiled and gave me a warm hug.

My mother, seeing us talking quietly, came over and asked "What are you two talking about?" We told her and she also reminded me to be careful when I am out. That I had met Miss Thornton also impressed her, but she didn't ask for any details. This didn't surprise me, as my mother seems to trust me a lot. And besides that, she knew that I would tell her more, when just she and I were alone together.

I had told Joseph about our evenings when I first invited him to come by. Since he didn't come that night, I hoped he would come tonight.

I hadn't told anyone in my family about Joseph possibly coming this evening. Still, I was disappointed that he hadn't shown up this night either; this meant that I had to find and talk to him again. And I didn't discuss this plan with anyone either.

The next morning, my mother asked me to run an errand for her. She had asked a lady who sews really well to make some outfits for my sister and me, and she wanted to know what progress the lady had made on the garments. I often run errands for my mother. She is a really shy person and doesn't like to leave the house much. After she first asked me to do errands for her, I soon realized it gave me a lot of space to do things I wanted to do. That's one reason why I learned to get around St. Louis on my own. I ride the trolleys and buses, and I walk around the city a lot. I feel quite comfortable in my own little world that I have made in St. Louis.

While I was out on the errand for my mother, I decided to stop by the Colored YMCA to see if Joseph was there. The man at the desk remembered me and said that Joseph had checked out of the Y some days ago. "But he'll be back," the man said to me. No wonder he had not shown up at my house—he had left the city!

I decided that the next day I would revisit Miss Thornton.

She smiled when she saw me. She was again out in her front yard, wearing a dress that had big red and yellow flowers on it. I almost matched what she had on, as I was wearing yellow shorts with a white blouse and my red and white saddle shoes—my school shoes, not my tennis shoes. Her pressed hair just touched the neck of her dress.

I explained to her that I had told my father about meeting her and that he was going to make a point of coming to see her soon, perhaps after summer school was over. She smiled her nice smile at that idea and said she looked forward to seeing him.

I had been thinking about what Mr. Nesby had told me and what I had read about the WPA at the library. I asked Miss Thornton to tell me if she had had anything to do with it—the WPA, that is. Hearing that question, she just stopped and stared at me. "How...what do you know about the WPA?"

"Well, I learned that Mr. Nesby had been part of the WPA, and I also went to the library, to see if there were books on the WPA there."

"You are just full of surprises, little girl!"

"Thank you—I think. What do you mean, Miss Thornton, about me being 'full of surprises'?"

"I haven't had much experience with young girls who seemed to be so independent and curious, that's all."

I smiled at that. I was secretly very happy that a grown-up had seen me that way.

Then Miss Thornton told me about her experiences in the WPA from 1937 to 1939. She said to me, "Well, here is a bit of what happened to me, and how I met Mr. Nesby.

"I worked at Lincoln University in Pennsylvania as a clerk, because that was my way of earning money to live in the North. The room I found to live in was close to the university, and it did not cost me a lot to rent. It was pretty daring of me, especially as a single woman, to leave my home in the South. I just couldn't live there anymore. She paused for a moment.

"I just couldn't stay in the South any longer, especially after I learned from some people that Negroes by the thousands were moving north—to get away from the oppressive, hard, unfriendly-to-Negroes living conditions in the South. I realized that I wanted to leave also. Having heard that Philadelphia (the nearest big city to Lincoln University) is called the City of Brotherly Love, seemed like a good omen to me.

"But my true love was art, and even though everyone knew that artists didn't make much money, I wanted to try my hand at it. I was a pretty good painter—at least that was what people at home told me. My job at Lincoln allowed me to take care of myself while I checked out the possibility of becoming an artist through the WPA.

"I found that, near where I lived, there was a WPA workshop where artists were learning to do printmaking. Well, I never knew anything about prints; let alone how to make them. I found the studio and I talked my way into the space where several artists were experimenting with new techniques of printmaking. Now, that was a pretty hard thing for me to do, because I am a woman."

I asked her to explain what a "print" was.

She said. "It is a way to make a picture that lets you make multiple copies of it. You make the original on a silk screen or a block of wood, then either press ink through the screen onto paper, or you put ink on the block and then press paper on it to make a copy.

"While you may not know it, Pauline Estelle, women often have a hard time doing things that men do. Men often look down on women wanting to do things that they do— like printmaking in this case. Nevertheless, I persisted and, little by little, the few men who worked in this studio got to know me. They let me make my own prints, and not just be their assistant. It was a very happy time for me, just being in the studio and working side by side with them. They were some pretty amazing artists, and Mr. Nesby was one of them. That's how I met him.

"I had my clerking job at the university and I was able to do art at the WPA printmaking studio in the evenings and on weekends. Now that I think about it, it was an unusual combination of careers. After about five years in Philadelphia, I decided to move to St. Louis, and here I am."

I wondered why she moved, but I didn't ask. Instead I said, "Boy, oh boy! Thank you very much for telling me all of these things about what you did."

She smiled and said, "I am happy to." I ventured to ask her what she did in St. Louis and did she like it here?

She said, "St. Louis was very much a southern city, and there were things that colored people couldn't do here, such as like eat in restaurants, and places where they could not go, like the Fox Theater, and places where they could not live, like near Washington University, but, all in all, it was way better than living in the deep South. The Ville was a perfect community (something my mother had said).

"When my aunt died, I got her house in Lewis Place, and I am still an artist and I make prints. Awhile back I had some of my prints in a group show. That's where I met your father. He was there with Mr. Carpenter, one of the art teachers at Sumner High School."

"I would like to see your work some day, Miss Thornton, but not today. Thank you very much for your time and your very interesting stories."

Then I took off to complete my errand for my mother and head for home.

During dinner, we listened to the news and some music. My sister and I washed the dishes fast, because that evening, rather than sit on the front lawn, water it, and play with our friends after dark, we were going to the Municipal Opera.

We dressed up, my father in a jacket and tie. My mother wore a nice blue seersucker dress and my sister and I wore matching, blue-striped dresses with white Peter Pan collars. As we didn't have a car, we took the bus out to Forest Park. Even though our seats at the opera were pretty high up from the stage, it made little difference to us. I loved the singing and dancing, eating ice cream on a stick, and eating popcorn. It was a very special evening.

We got home quite late and the next morning I didn't get up as early as I usually do. After breakfast, I decided to stay close to home and just walk over to Tandy Park. The Bookmobile might be there and I could check out a book to read for the Read Away Vacation Club. I put on my blue shorts again and paired them with a seersucker blouse with no collar. I did not wear socks with my tennis shoes that morning. Later I decided not to do that again because without socks, my feet really sweat.

The Bookmobile was there. I found two books that looked interesting to read and, when I finished reading them, I'd be able to add them to my already long list of books I had read that summer.

I took the library books home and, before reading them, I decided to review what I had learned so far. I pulled out my hidden notebook and started to bring it up to date.

I now knew:

1. Why Miss Thornton was at Lincoln University in PA

2. About Mr. Nesby, the WPA and his connection to Miss Rose Thornton

3. About Miss Rose Thornton and her connection to the WPA and Mr. Nesby

I still didn't know any more about Joseph and his connection with Miss Thornton and Mr. Nesby, nor why he left town.

In looking at the columns I had made in my notebook, I realized that I wasn't using them and that all I needed to do was write what I learned about each of my characters in a sentence or two by their names. I really liked the idea of columns, but they were useless to me, at least at this point.

It seemed now that I was at a place in my investigation where I really needed to talk to Joseph. Where was he and when was he going to show up again, I wondered to myself. Since I didn't know the answers to either one, I thought that I would go back down the street to see Mrs. Fox, and ask her sons if they had seen him lately. As I approached Mrs. Fox's house, I saw Robert and John Fox just leaving.

"Hi, Robert. Hi, John." They looked at me like they didn't know who I was, or at least they pretended not to, but that didn't stop me.

"Have you seen that man I asked you about the other day? I know his name now."

They both stopped and looked at me. I thought to myself, if Mrs. Fox had been there with them, they would have treated me nicer, but that still didn't stop me.

"His name is Joseph. He is staying—or was staying—at the Y. Have you seen him?"

Now they both looked at me with, maybe, a little respect? I thought to myself, I bet they were surprised that I knew the mystery man's name. They glanced at each other and then said to me, almost in unison, "No, we haven't seen him, and we haven't heard any more about him. How do you know that his name is Joseph?"

I told them—real fast—how I had found out where he was staying and how I found out his name and that I had talked to him, but that I hadn't seen him for about a week and I would like to talk to him again.

"Wow, Pauline Estelle, you know a lot more about him now than we do. We're sorry we can't help you anymore."

I reminded them that Robert had told me about the gathering in front of the high school, and that Joseph had said something to the crowd about having good news. I told the boys that seemed to me like something important to learn more about.

They agreed and said to me, "If you find out anything more, let us know, and if we find out anything about him, we will let you know."

After a short visit with Mrs. Fox, I decided to go to Tandy Park, sit on the tennis bleachers in the sun and think about what to do next. Mr. Hudlin was there again, coaching some tennis players. He didn't pay any attention to me, which was just fine with me. I knew that my father was arranging for him to give my sister and me tennis lessons, but those lessons hadn't started yet. I just sat there on the bleachers thinking and thinking about what I should do next?

Then an idea seemed to just pop into my mind—an idea that actually felt bigger than Joseph wanting to meet Mr. Nesby and Miss Thornton. I found the idea intriguing (another new word for me).

I remembered that Mr. Nesby and Miss Thornton had come to St. Louis from someplace else. I remembered that Miss Thornton had told me about why she went to Philadelphia. But I had not asked Mr. Nesby if he too had left the South, and if he had left the South for reasons other than going to Lincoln University.

Lots to think about. I went back home and spent the rest of the day in my room or out in the back yard, reading and just thinking about what to do with my idea.

I let my mother know that I was home. She was wearing a pretty, flowered cotton dress that I liked. She just let me be. It was very nice of her not to try and talk to me, or ask me to do any chores, or anything like that. It was as if she knew that I just needed to spend a lazy day thinking.

The next day was a little overcast; it looked like it might rain, but that didn't stop me from deciding to go to the library again. After cleaning up my side of the room and helping clean up the kitchen after breakfast, I went to the big library downtown, once again taking the bus and trolley.

This time, I asked the librarian if there were any books about Negroes moving from the South to up North. I thought that someone might have written about Negroes moving around the country after the Emancipation. This time, the librarian was not able to help me. She could not find any books about that.

"Are you sure?"

"Yes" she said. "The only things that I can find are the pamphlets about the WPA." She had remembered my request from the other day. I looked at more pamphlets, trying to understand, but I could not to find anything on what was still just an unclear idea in my head.

I was really disappointed. I thought that the library had books on everything I would want to know about. But that didn't seem to be the case when I asked about Negroes moving from the South to the North.

At this point, my idea, which had been just an idea, now sprang fully into my mind. I would make my own pamphlet on Negros moving out of the South! I would ask my parents, and some of my parents' friends, and perhaps some neighbors, about what had brought them to St. Louis. I thought I would start with my mother and father.

It was another hot, high-humidity St. Louis evening. My father was idly watering the grass once again, when I asked him to tell me about when and how he got to St. Louis.

My father obliged. "I was born in Rhode Island and raised in Boston where I went to Boston Latin high school, after which I joined the Army. After I got out of the Army, at the end of WWI, I went to Lincoln University in Pennsylvania. I earned my BA in English. Then I got my

Masters Degree from Columbia University in New York in 1926.

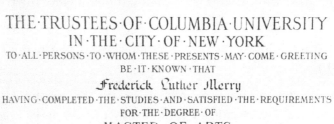

THE·TRUSTEES·OF·COLUMBIA·UNIVERSITY
IN·THE·CITY·OF·NEW·YORK
TO·ALL·PERSONS·TO·WHOM·THESE·PRESENTS·MAY·COME·GREETING
BE·IT·KNOWN·THAT
Frederick Luther Merry
HAVING·COMPLETED·THE·STUDIES·AND·SATISFIED·THE·REQUIREMENTS
FOR·THE·DEGREE·OF
MASTER · OF · ARTS
HAS·ACCORDINGLY·BEEN·ADMITTED·TO·THAT·DEGREE·WITH·ALL·THE
RIGHTS·PRIVILEGES·AND·IMMUNITIES·THEREUNTO·APPERTAINING
IN·WITNESS·WHEREOF·WE·HAVE·CAUSED·THIS·DIPLOMA·TO·BE·SIGNED
BY·THE·PRESIDENT·OF·THE·UNIVERSITY·AND·BY·THE·DEAN·OF·TEACHERS
COLLEGE·AND·OUR·CORPORATE·SEAL·TO·BE·HERETO·AFFIXED·IN·THE
CITY·OF·NEW·YORK·ON·THE · SECOND · DAY·OF · JUNE · IN·THE
YEAR·OF·OUR·LORD·ONE·THOUSAND·NINE·HUNDRED·AND·TWENTY-SIX

DEAN

PRESIDENT

"I went to several states looking for work, including Mississippi, where I taught English for a year at Tugaloo University. Since I grew up in the North I found it very difficult to live in the deep South where I had to step off the sidewalk if a white person passed by. I couldn't eat in restaurants there, and Negroes lived in a hard part of town. Racial segregation was grossly unfair. All of these things made me angry, and I was constantly afraid for my safety. So, after that year, I went back to Boston and did some substitute teaching there at Boston Latin—but I didn't want to stay there."

"Why didn't you want to stay in Boston, Daddy?"

"I just wanted to live somewhere else, and I had heard that Negro teachers got paid a pretty good salary in St. Louis. So, after marrying your mother, we moved here."

"So in other words, the good salary for Negro teachers is why we live here now?"

"Yes, that about sums it up: money and relative safety for all of us."

"Do you know about other colored people moving from the South to the North?"

"I think a lot of Negroes are moving out of the South, and I think that it is a good thing."

It was getting late, so I put off asking my mother the same questions. Besides, I could ask her in the morning. I wanted to know her version of why we were in St. Louis.

In the morning, I got up and put on a clean old cotton school dress as I didn't plan to go anywhere far from my house that day—not to the big library, or even Tandy Park. I combed my hair, wishing that I could go to the hairdresser soon, because my hair was beginning to look bad in my eyes.

It surprised my mother that I wasn't going off to the park. She wondered aloud to me, "What do you plan to do today, Pauline Estelle?"

"I'd like to ask you about something that I just thought of the other day."

"Well, what is it?"

First of all, you need to know that my mother was really pretty. Her skin color was several shades lighter than my father's, mine and my sister's. But her hair was like mine—it had to be pressed to give the appearance of being straight. And she had dimples in both cheeks and her daughters didn't get any! Her teeth were white and straight. She told me once that she had been taken to Johns Hopkins Hospital in Baltimore when she was a child, and the nurses and doctors had come into her examining room to admire her pretty teeth. She was lucky to keep them all of her life. Both my aunts, her sisters, had had all of their teeth removed. I asked them why, and they said it wasn't possible to get fillings back then.

I liked how she looked. But this morning she was wearing a plain, soft light brown, button-down the front cotton dress that wasn't very pretty.

We sat in the kitchen, where it was nice and cool. I brought her up to date on what I had learned about Mr. Nesby, Miss Thornton, and the visitor Joseph. I told her that it had occurred to me to wonder about colored people coming to St. Louis. And that led me to wondering if all of these colored people coming to St. Louis were somehow related to why Joseph was interested in Mr. Nesby and Miss Thornton in addition to their WPA connections. Then I stopped talking and took a sip of the cold milk my mother had poured for me.

My mother just looked at me for a moment, as she drank her iced coffee; then she smiled.

"My goodness, Pauline Estelle, you are one amazing little girl. I had no idea that you had done all of that, or all that was going on in your mind."

I shyly thanked her and said, "I am not done yet. I really do not know if my idea is a good one, but it just popped into my head while I was trying to figure out the Mr. Nesby, Miss Thornton, Joseph connection."

My mother again said that I was amazing, and that I was on the right track.

"Yes, many colored people were moving north from the South, not only to St. Louis but other northern cities like New York, Chicago, and other western cities such as Los Angeles. Like your father and me."

Then, before I could ask her version of why she and my father came to St. Louis, she began:

"Before I tell you about how we got here, let me remind you a little about myself. If I haven't already told you or, if I have, it won't hurt you to hear it again."

"Okay." I said, happy to hear what she had to say.

"You know my sisters, your Aunts Irene and Carrie. You have met your Uncle Carroll, but not Elijah. He died some while ago. Carroll was a handyman, and Elijah had been a chef in Baltimore. Our parents Isabel and Josiah Stricklin sent the girls—us—to college. Irene went to Delaware State. I went to boarding school there and then on to Pratt Institute to study Home Economics. Your Aunt Carrie went to Hampton Institute for nursing. Our parents believed in educating their girls.

My aunt Carrie
(c. 1910 at Hampton)

"Then, because I didn't want to be a teacher, after Pratt Institute I worked at Harlem Hospital as a dietitian. It was there I met my first husband, Dr. Sam Stuard, the father of your half-sister Betty Jane, who as you know is living with Ben and Irene in Chestertown.

After he and I divorced, I met and married your father. After our marriage, we honeymooned in Paris. And that was quite some experience!

"Because he didn't want to go back to Boston or to anywhere in the South to teach, we came to St. Louis, mainly because colored teachers were said to earn pretty good salaries here. So that's how we got here.

"So, Pauline Estelle, you *are* on to something. Thousands of colored people moved and probably still are moving out of the South to places north where living conditions, jobs, and housing are better for colored people. It's still not easy, though. As you can see, we live in a segregated community and you go to a segregated school, but even at that, we are better off here than somewhere in the South. It's not perfect, but…."

At that point, I smiled and thanked my mother for telling me about how we got here. Perhaps that was why other colored people came as well.

"You are smart, and I am proud that you thought about something that might not be obvious to kids your age. Okay, my smart little girl, what's next on your agenda?"

"I plan to ask more adults in The Ville why they had come to St. Louis."

She smiled and said, "Keep me posted."

I stayed home that day and made a list of the questions that I would ask some of the adults in The Ville.

My questions were:

- Did you come to St. Louis from somewhere else?
- When did you come?
- Why did you come?
- Are you glad that you came?

I thought that these four questions would be good, even though I wasn't sure what I would do with their answers. Anyway, it was a start.

I put my list of questions in my notebook and then spent the rest of the day not doing much of anything. I read one of the two books that I had gotten from the library. I had lunch with my mother and sister, and in the evening, after dinner, we went outside to enjoy another hot St. Louis evening. We played, my father watered the grass, and my mother chatted with the neighbors, all the things we regularly did.

The next morning after breakfast, I combed my hair, put on a white blouse and some green striped shorts, white socks and my tennis shoes. I put my note book in a little bag with a pencil, yelled good-bye to my mother and out the door I went. I was ready to go to work on my project.

I turned left out of our front door and headed toward Homer G Phillips Hospital, City Hospital Number 2, one of only two for colored people. The other colored hospital in St. Louis (where I had been born) was People's Hospital (closer to downtown, rather than in The Ville). As I was walking, I saw a neighbor sitting on her porch. I crossed the street and greeted her.

"Good Morning Mrs. Todd, I am Pauline Estelle and I live up the street."

She looked at me for a moment and said, "Girl, I know who you are, you are Mr. Merry's daughter."

"Yes ma'am, I am doing a little summer project (I really didn't know what to call what I was doing, so I called it a project.) and I wonder if you would mind answering some questions for me? And if you don't mind, I am going to write your answers in my notebook under your name. Will that be alright?"

"Sho' nuf honey, ask away. And you can write my answers in your notebook."

"Okay, and thanks for letting me write your answers down." I said and proceeded to ask:

"Did you come to St. Louis from somewhere else?"

"Yes, I came from Mississippi."

"When did you come?"

"I have been here in St. Louis since 1930."

"Why did you come?"

"I came here because my family wanted to leave Mississippi on account of the hard living conditions for coloreds there. We worked hard, but had nothing to show for it. There were seven of us and we all lived in a three room shack that could hardly stand up. We heard that some of our neighbors had left, or were thinking about leaving, so we decided to leave too."

"Are you glad that you came?"

"Baby, do birds sing in the trees? It is the best thing we ever done, although I do miss some of my folks we left behind."

I thanked her for helping me and said good-bye. Then I was off to talk to the next person who would take time to talk to me. That next person was a man who worked at the high school where my father taught. He was out working in his yard.

"Hi Mr. Moore, I am working on a little summer project and I wonder if you'll answer some questions I have?" He looked at me and asked, "Ain't you Mr. Merry's girl?"

"Yes sir, I am and if it is alright with you, I would like to write your answers down in this note book here."

He responded kinda gruffly, "What do you want to know?"

"Did you come to St. Louis from somewhere else?"

"I came here from Alabama."

"When did you come?"

"Oh, around 1934."

"Why did you come?"

"Girl, you sho asking a lot of questions."

"Yes sir. Why did you come?"

He thought for a moment, took a handkerchief out of his pocket, wiped his face, and began to talk.

"It's kinda a long story, but me and my family had decided to leave Alabama. We came here because, at the train station, we saw lines at three windows, and one of us stood in a line at each window, and the first person to get to a window is where we would go. My cousin got to the St. Louis window first, so we all went over to that line and that's why we got to St. Louis. We didn't care whether we was going to New York, Chicago, or St. Louis. We just knew that we had to get out of Alabama."

"Are you glad that you came?"

"Of course we're glad. Up here we had a chance to live a better life. We could get jobs that paid good—for colored people anyways—and while St. Louis is sorta like the South, it sure ain't like Alabama. There we had to get off the side walk if a white man walked by. We was always afraid of someone we knew being lynched for no reason, except that some white person wanted to hurt—no, wanted to kill some poor innocent Black person. Our houses were on the edge of town and they were horrible, the roads weren't paved and the schools—could hardly call what we went to schools—no books, no supplies, no nuthin."

I thanked him kindly and told him that I would tell my father that I had chatted with him, and that he had been really nice to answer my questions.

"Tell Mr. Merry and yo Momma hello for me." I said that I would.

I walked on, and the next person I talked to was from Georgia and she had been in St. Louis for what she said was a long time. Her name was Mrs. Grimes. She, too, was sitting on her front porch, and when I asked her if I could ask her some questions and write her answers in my notebook.

She said, "O' course, chil.' My husband and our four children had left the Peach State in order to find better living conditions and better work. First, I worked as a maid for a white family, and Mr. Grimes worked at Scullin Steel Mill. I didn't like my work, because I didn't like working for white folks. Even though they were sorta 'nice' to me, I had my pride and working for white folks made me think less of myself than I liked. As for Mr. Grimes, he hated working at Scullin because the work was hard, hot, and dangerous. And he learned that even though he was doing the same work as the white men, he was getting paid less. But still, we were better off than in Georgia."

As for her children going to school here: "I know that my kids are so much better off in the schools here, even though the schools are segregated. They have some really good teachers, and all of my children want to be teachers."

"My father is a teacher."

Mrs. Grimes said, "See there, I told you so." She smiled at me and I smiled back, thanking her for taking the time to talk to me.

I spent the rest of the day talking to other people in my neighborhood, asking them my four questions. I didn't even stop to go home for lunch. I was working on my project.

Almost all of them knew, or knew of, my father, which was nice, and even those who didn't were nice to take their time to talk to me.

I spent the next day doing the same thing. Walking all over The Ville, I asked my four questions of about ten more people. Among them were several teachers, a nurse, the father of a friend who was a doctor, and the lady who worked behind the counter at Billy Burke's—that's the restaurant in The Ville, next to the Comet Movie Theater. Everybody's answers were almost the same, or had the same theme (a term I learned later). So here, in summary, is what I found out:

1. Did you come to St. Louis from somewhere else?
   Yes, we came from Georgia, Alabama, Mississippi—all states that been the Confederate States of the Civil War.

2. When did you come?
   We started coming here after WWI in the mid-twenties and early-thirties.

3. Why did you come?
   We came because living in the South was so very difficult for colored people. Our houses were shacks, our schools were poor, *we* were poor. We were forced to live in segregated parts of town—mostly in the country or on farms, often on the same plantations where our grandparents, or even our parents, had been slaves. The roads were unpaved and medical care was mostly non-existent, or hard to come by, when it was available.

4. Are you glad that you came?
   One lady's answer summed it all up for me. She said, "Does the sun come up every morning, little girl?"

I decided to tell my mother what I had discovered. I read to her from my notes, and she was amazed and impressed by my work. She gave it a grown up name, calling it my research. I smiled and basked in her praise of me and what I had found. We discussed things like poor housing, no work and segregation, as things that had bought people out of the South. As my mother and I talked about my work, I came more to understand that for some, moving north had saved their lives. For others, I learned, life was still very hard, but it was much better than it had been in the South. My mother gave me a kiss on my cheek, and I went up to my room to put my notebook away again in its secret place.

So, now I had all of this information and nothing to do with it until Joseph showed up. I really wanted to find out what he was doing, and if perhaps what I had found out in any way might contribute to his work. I had no idea if it would or not.

Another week went by, and I continued with my reading and going to Tandy Park. My father set a date for me to start my tennis lessons with Mr. Hudlin. That's something I'm looking forward to, although I am a little afraid of having to show Mr. Hudlin how little I know about the game. It's August already. Summer will be over soon. Then I'll be back in school, which I am looking forward to.

I like going to school and being in the classroom. My father is a teacher, and my Aunt Irene and Uncle Ben, who live in Maryland, are teachers, and they seem to like their work. I have paid a lot of attention to how my teachers behave toward each other, and with us students. School is a place I almost always look forward to going to, especially when things can get a little boring. Curiously, I never imagined I might become a teacher.

Then, when I least expected it, who should come walking up the street to our house one Sunday evening after dinner? Yes, you guessed it. It was Joseph!

I had not recognized him at first when he paused in front of our house, but, when I did, I yelled "Joseph, Joseph, Joseph!" With each repetition of his name, I yelled louder. "Joseph!" Then I started shouting, "Where have you been? What have you been doing? "Will you visit with us for a bit?"

Of course, my parents and the neighbors sitting outside with us were curious. Who was this young man they had never seen, but who definitely seemed to be known by me.

"Wait—let me go get Mrs. Nesby." So off I ran two doors down the street and called for Mrs. Nesby.

"Mrs. Nesby, he's here!" I shouted. She came to the door, looked straight at me and held her finger up to her lips, indicating that I should quiet down. So I said in a whisper, "Mrs. Nesby, Joseph is here. Please come over and talk to him with us." She said, "I'll tell Mr. Nesby and we will both come over. It'll only take a few minutes."

I ran back home. In the meantime, my parents and the neighbors had introduced themselves to Joseph. My mother asked him to have a seat. She and he both smiled at that. My father offered him a glass of his home-made root beer (one of my father's favorite summer hobbies). After he accepted a cool glass of root beer, we all got comfortable and eagerly waited for Joseph to tell us what was going on.

It was around four o'clock Sunday afternoon. I only wished that Miss Thornton were with us too, but I knew that she would somehow be included in future conversations, perhaps when I went to visit her with my father.

Before Joseph could start talking though, my father asked, "Young man, what is your surname?"

"Oh, I am sorry Mr. Merry, my last name is Edwards. I am Joseph Edwards."

By then, Mr. and Mrs. Nesby had joined us. Joseph stood quickly and said, "Oh, Mrs. Nesby, I didn't mean to startle you before, and I apologize to you for that."

And to me he said that he had apologized to the desk man at the Y for not leaving his room key. At that, my parents looked at me in surprise, but didn't ask then what that was about, although I thought they might be asking me later.

"Well," with a deep breath, he started in response to my father's question. "I am a graduate student at Lincoln University—the one in Pennsylvania, not the one in Jefferson City, Missouri. I am working on my Master's degree in Teaching and Art History. My 'Art History' part is on Negro Art of the WPA. I will be doing my student teaching on that subject—I hope here in St. Louis at Stowe Teacher's College, just around the corner."

At the mention of Lincoln my father stopped with his glass mid-way to his mouth, and said, "Well, well, well, what a coincidence, Joseph. That's my Alma Mater." Joseph and my father looked at each other and grinned. Mr. Nesby spoke up, saying, "Oh my goodness! All three of us went to Lincoln."

The three of them began to talk about their experiences there and, for a while, all of us sitting around them heard things about Lincoln that my father had never shared with us before. This included the fact that he had joined Alpha Phi Alpha Fraternity there—a great source of pride for him. After a bit, the three of them agreed that they would talk about Lincoln another time, but that this evening Joseph would talk to us all about what he was doing and what he needed.

Joseph turned to all of us again and said he had learned that Philadelphia had been one of the centers in the country that had WPA Art studios. These were places where colored artists were invited to participate because artists had to eat too, as was pointed out by someone who defended the inclusion of artists in the WPA work pool.

At many of these centers, Joseph explained, new techniques of making prints were developed and, while many of the prints were lost over time, the Library of Congress still has examples of some really fine print work that was done at them. He rattled off many names that no one else present had ever heard of, and he said that was exactly why he was doing his thesis on them. He wanted to preserve as much of their work and their legacy as possible.

"How did it happen that you came to St. Louis?" my father asked.

"Well sir, that is interesting. As I was doing my research about the Philadelphia center, it occurred to me that I might visit other centers, but they no longer exist. I thought, why not try and locate some of the print makers who were still alive. Somehow I discovered that Mr. Nesby and Miss Thornton had come to St. Louis and were living here. I decided that I should go visit them, which is why I am here."

"And your student teaching assignment at Stowe?" my father asked.

"Well that's pretty interesting, too," Joseph said, "and I really am in luck that I found the opportunity to do that in the fall here in St. Louis. So, as they say, two birds with one stone."

Mr. Nesby finally spoke up and said, "You really did some investigating. I have not seen any of my work for years. I don't know where most of it is." He paused, then said, "Now that I think about it, I do have a box somewhere that holds a few prints." At hearing that, Joseph nearly jumped out of his seat.

"You do, sir? How wonderful that you have some of your work. That is just wonderful!" He then asked shyly, "May I be allowed to see them?"

"Of course you can, young man. I think that some of it is pretty good, if I do say so myself."

"Ruth," he said to Mrs. Nesby, "when would be a good day for Joseph come and see what I have in that box in the back of the closet in the hallway?"

"Box in the closet?" she thought out loud. "Oh, that box. I've always wondered what was in that box. Now I'll finally get a chance to see for myself."

So it was arranged for Joseph to visit the Nesbys during the following week. Naturally, I asked them if I could be there when the box's contents were revealed.

Mr. Nesby looked over at me. "Well of course you can, Pauline Estelle. If it weren't for you, we might not have gathered here this evening. And even though I don't feel all that well, it will be nice to kinda re-live some of what I did years ago as an artist."

Then Joseph said, "I have already talked to Miss Thornton about her work, and now that I am back in town, I will make an appointment to go see her this week. I believe that even though she is a woman, and had a bit of a hard time being accepted by the men in the studio, her prints were just as good as those of the men she learned under. And later, she even taught some novel craft techniques she had developed when new print makers came to the studio."

I was beside myself with pride and happiness. This was so wonderful, having Joseph unexpectedly showing up (which, of course, I had been secretly hoping he would) and hearing about his studies, and Miss Thornton's and Mr. Nesby's art.

Then my mother spoke up, "Joseph, I bet you didn't know that you have had a positive influence on Pauline Estelle as well." I shyly hung my head a little as everyone turned to look at me, even my sister and father.

"Well Pauline Estelle, tell him what you thought of and what you have been doing," she said, urging me on. "Tell him, and all of us, what you have been doing these past several weeks."

Well, she really put me on the spot, but I went ahead. Actually, I really wanted to. She gave me an excuse, or opportunity, or any way, permission, to talk about what I had done.

It was still light out and even though we were all dressed in light summer clothes, we were still hot. My mother got everyone another glass of whatever it was that they had been drinking—iced tea, water, or my father's root beer. Then they all turned to listen to me.

I began talking, "After Joseph had spoken to Mrs. Nesby and Miss Thornton, I got the idea in my head that there might be some connection between *who* he was looking for, and *what* he was looking for, even though I wasn't quite sure what that connection was. Mr. Nesby and Miss Thornton had come to St. Louis from somewhere else. Then I asked my mother and father. They had they come to St. Louis from somewhere else. So with just knowing that four adults had come from somewhere else got me thinking that perhaps a lot of grownups here had come from somewhere else. I mean, they hadn't been born here in St. Louis. With that in mind, what I did was ask a lot of grownups here in The Ville if they had come from somewhere else. And don't you know, almost every adult I talked to had come from somewhere else!"

I was surprised that no one had stopped me so far, so I went on to tell them all about my four questions:

"These are the questions I asked every adult that I spoke to:"

1. Did you come to St. Louis from somewhere else?

2. When did you come?

3. Why did you come?

4. Are you glad that you came?

"And what were the answers?" someone asked.

At that point, it was now getting dark, I was tired and I was happy when my mother said, "Why don't we call it an evening right now. With Joseph coming and all of you listening to him and Pauline Estelle, I think we should continue this conversation tomorrow. What do you all think?"

Everyone agreed that we would gladly continue this story tomorrow evening. My father said that he would see if he could get Miss Thornton to join us.

Joseph said good night to us all, and off he went down the street, back to the colored Y. And Mr. and Mrs. Nesby and the neighbors all went on home.

As I was going to my room, my mother said to me, "You did some impressive work, Pauline Estelle." She smiled, kissed me on the forehead and said, "Good night" to me, and then to my sister. My father yelled his "Good night" to us as well. We all went to sleep on another hot St. Louis summer night.

The next evening, just as planned, Joseph, my parents and sister, some of the neighbors, Mr. and Mrs. Nesby gathered on our front lawn. Best of all, Miss Rose Thornton arrived, a little after 6 p.m. We sat in lawn chairs and each had a cool drink. Miss Thornton had to be introduced to everyone, except Joseph, my father and me. She told everyone about how she, too, was an artist and had been part of the WPA artist printmaking studio in Philadelphia. She and Mr. Nesby were very happy to see one another again.

Then my mother urged me to go on telling about my interviews and what I learned. Miss Thornton had to be caught up on one or two points, but when she was, she understood completely what I had done. She said that I was very clever to have made the "new to St. Louis" connection. And after telling everyone a bit more about my interviews of folks using my four questions, I summarized for them that all of these people had moved north simply *for a better life!*

Joseph said he was amazed by what he called my 'scholarship,' and he asked my permission to use my notes and add several paragraphs, perhaps putting them into a story in his thesis about the exodus from the South to the North of thousands and thousands of colored people. He said that in his thesis, he would make a connection between this exodus and the role of the WPA in helping Negroes improve their lives, especially artists, writers and craftsmen.

Joseph added that at the beginning of the Second World War the government stopped paying for WPA jobs, as now there was a war to win and lots of other government funded jobs were available.

"I would be pleased and honored, Joseph, to give you my notes on what I had found, if you think that it would help you get your degree and make your work better."

So that's my story about the mystery man who came to visit Mr. Nesby. I learned a lot about the people who lived in The Ville and how their lives affected me—directly and indirectly. I liked that. I also liked that I had ventured out into the community with a project that I had thought of, all by myself.

Now I was ready for another adventure!

* * * * *

Coda

Later on Joseph did start his student teaching at Stowe Teachers College. His supervising teacher encouraged him to create a section of the course he was teaching to feature the history of Black artists in the WPA.

He arranged to have the works of Miss Thornton and Mr. Nesby shown at a reception at the college—this was the "good news" that Joseph had spoken about. Most everyone went to the reception—the neighbors on St. Ferdinand, many of the people I had interviewed, teachers from Sumner and professors from Stowe.

Miss Thornton just seemed to glow under all of the attention she received. (My father, by the way, never did take me to visit her. I guess he thought that he didn't need to, as I had found her myself.) Mr. Nesby, who was suffering from tuberculosis, managed to look healthy for that evening, and he certainly was happy with all of the recognition that was being bestowed upon him. Mrs. Nesby never left his side.

The Black newspaper—*The St. Louis Argus* covered the reception and even the *St. Louis Post Dispatch* had a tiny article about the event at Stowe, the two Black printmakers and the WPA.

Some Questions to Think About

1. Describe your 'neighborhood.' Is it part of a big city, or a small town, a suburb, or a rural area? What is the traffic like where you live?

2. What do you like best about where you live? What do you dislike? What would you like to be different...?

3. Do you know *why* you live where you live? Who can you ask?

4. How do you get to school? Walk, alone or with friends? Are you driven by your parent, or by someone else? Or do you ride a bus? (Or maybe, if you live in a rural area you might ride a horse to school!)

5. Describe your classmates. Is there someone in your class you'd like to get to know better? What can you do about that?

6. Do you know where the grown-ups who take care of you came from, originally? Who could you ask?

7. Have you ever had a mystery to solve? If 'yes', how did you solve it?

8. What kinds of books do you like to read? Do you have, and ever use, a library card? Can you just imagine what you might discover by going there?

9. What has been your favorite part of *"Where Have You Been?"*

10. In this story I asked a series of questions of a bunch of adults. Is there some question, or more than one, that *you* would like to ask some adults?

If You Want to Lean More
Here are two good sources of information:

Langston Hughes, *Poetry for Young People* edited by David Roessel & Arnold Rampersad & illustrated by Benny Andrews

Anne E Schraff, *The Life of Dr. Charles Drew: Blood Bank Innovator*

I'd love to hear from you, my readers.
You may contact me, the author, by emailing me at:
PaulineEstelleMerry@GreatTalesToldWell.com

Map: "My Country"

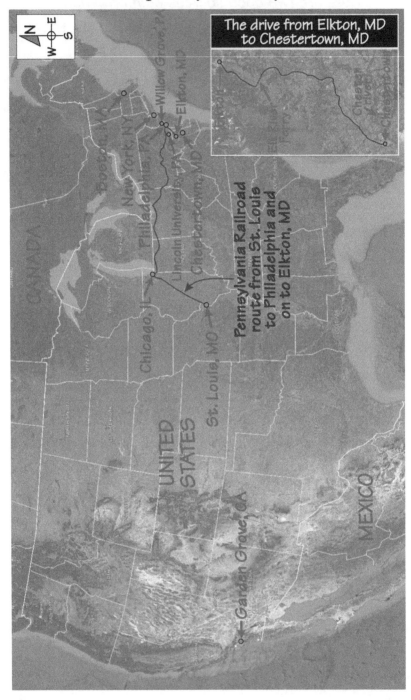

The drive from Elkton, MD to Chestertown, MD

Willow Grove, PA
Elkton, MD
Boston, MA
New York, NY
Philadelphia, PA
Lincoln University, PA
Chestertown, MD
CANADA
Chicago, IL
St. Louis, MO
UNITED STATES
Garden Grove, CA
MEXICO

Pennsylvania Railroad route from St. Louis to Philadelphia and on to Elkton, MD

Elkton Ferry
Chester River
Chestertown

Story 4
Summer Time

School was out and my sister Freddie, my mother and I made plans to travel to Chestertown, Md., my mother's birthplace. That place, for me, was magical, a place where I felt free. I could dream and make up things about myself that were outside my usual way of being. I didn't share these ideas and thoughts with others though. Not sharing allowed me to feel free without apology or explanation. Life outside the confines of The Ville, away from my school, All Saints Episcopal Church, even my friends—and especially my father—that was what Chestertown was about for me. This story tells about what happened on my trip there in 1948.

I loved my father, I guess, but, because I was afraid of him, I didn't feel like I could really be myself around him. I guess he loved me. He provided for me, my mother and sister, yet I felt a distance between us, a feeling that I wished was not there. So just the thought of going to Chestertown was not only thrilling for me, but a relief. The prospect of learning new things, seeing new things and the opportunity to be a "different" person myself was so very satisfying! I hoped that this summer in Chestertown would bring a new adventure. And as it turns out, It did.

* * * * *

"Are you awake?" I whispered to my sister.

"Yes. Are you?"

It was the night before we were leaving for our trip. We were so excited that we whispered back and forth for a long time about what we planned to do when we got to Chestertown. Our mother, hearing us, said, "I think that you two need to try and get some sleep. We will be leaving very early in the morning, and you'll need to be well-rested."

"Okay, Mother Dear," we responded in unison. We fell so deeply asleep that come morning, mother had to gently

117

shake us to wake us up. For the trip, mother wore a beautiful navy blue linen dress and a hat with a small navy blue veil and white gloves. Her shoes were navy blue, too. Her hair was brushed up into a small pompadour. My sister and I wore similar seersucker dresses that buttoned to the waist with short sleeves, hers was yellow and mine was green, my favorite color. Our tennis shoes had been packed and we wore shiny patent leather Mary Jane shoes with white socks. The day before our hair had been pressed and curled. We thought we were *really* something!

With Daddy, the four of us walked toward the Page Avenue bus stop closest to our house on Hammett Place. My sister and I carried our own suitcase. Daddy carried Mother's. We boarded the bus and made our way to Union Station to catch the train. We left Daddy on the platform waving good-bye until we could no longer see him. The train slowly gathered speed, and we were on our way to Thirtieth Street Station in Philadelphia.

I knew that travel for us during this time in the United States was a mixture of forced segregation in the South and non-segregation in the north and west. Missouri had come into the Union as a border state which meant that some aspects of social and public living were segregated and some were not. Schools and housing were segregated. Public transportation was not in St. Louis—that is to say, colored people didn't have to ride in the back of the bus. Because we were north of the Mason Dixon Line, on the train we were able to sit where we wanted and could eat in the dining room without being restricted to tables set aside for each race, as restaurants in St, Louis were. I know, it's crazy, but having this kind of freedom at the beginning of our trip already set the stage for me to be in another world.

On this trip we sat in coach. My sister and I sat in a pair of seats in the row in front of the one occupied by our mother. She was lucky not to have to have someone sitting next to her, which meant that we essentially had four seats. Mother used the empty one beside her to hold two blankets and two pillows that the porter got for us, our sweaters, and our picnic lunch. The ride from St. Louis to Philadelphia was overnight. That meant that we had all day and the night to enjoy the trip. And we really did, partially because we had so much room. In addition, the train was air-conditioned. How nice it was not to be in the humid St. Louis summer heat. We would ride in cool comfort.

The train jerked once or twice and we were off, pulling slowly out of Union Station and then almost immediately we crossed the Mississippi River into Illinois. We looked out of the large windows as we passed through East St. Louis and then through farmland and small towns, soon arriving in Chicago, where a few got off but many more got on the train.

It was almost noon. Our mother asked the porter which direction the dining car was; he told us and she decided that we would go and have something to drink. That sounded good to us and somewhat excitedly, we found our way to the dining car, where our mother had iced tea and my sister and I had tall glasses of cold milk. The Black waiters were very nice, they seemed nicer than they had to be, perhaps because they were proud to see us there. Looking out of the windows, as we had our drinks at the table was so wonderful, seeing farms and farm animals and the occasional person out and about on a tractor, or just walking among rows of corn. The farms were so unlike what we normally saw that I could easily dream about living on one, although I had not the slightest idea about what that would be like.

After a while, because the dining car was about to close to prepare for dinner, we went back to our seats and ate the sandwiches that Mother had prepared. Many other passengers were eating out of boxes that contained their food as well. Mother said that we would have at least one meal in the dining car before we got to Philadelphia.

The rest of the day and into the evening, we gazed out of the window, took walks through the other coach cars, and even went through some sleeping cars on one round of walking. Someday we thought we too would get a sleeper and have a room with beds all to ourselves. My sister and I took turns sitting at the window, or one of us would go and sit by the window in the row that Mother occupied.

Sometimes we talked to each other and some of the other travelers. I had thought to bring a book to read, but found that looking out of the window was far more interesting than reading. Even though I loved reading, riding the train was far more exciting than having to make pictures in my mind as I read. As it started to get dark, the lights were lowered in the coach, and passengers began to settle down to sleep for the night.

We got as comfortable as we could with our pillows and blankets, fluffing them this way and that, until we were as satisfied as we could be, sitting up with our seat backs reclined as far as they could go. I did not fall asleep right away, and I don't think I slept the entire time. My sister let me sit by the window, so I could snuggle up to the cool window glass. The train seemed to fly during the night. I saw lights far off in the distance or, as we passed through towns the lights of train stations and of the small towns that we passed through, but did not stop. I wondered and made up stories about the people and their houses, and who and what they did. Sometimes I saw mothers with children. An old man standing alone. A young Black man with two small kids. The station attendant. Who were they? Why were they there? Were they happy or sad? Afraid or worried?

Finally morning came. As we were traveling east, I could see the sun coming up, and its brightness made me blink. This time we ate breakfast in the dining room. My mother had coffee, toast and eggs. My sister and I had milk and French toast. Back in our seats, we prepared to get off the train, as we would be arriving at the Thirtieth Street Station in Philadelphia shortly. When we did, we let others get off before we did, as we were in no real hurry. We were to be met by Mother's niece, our cousin Isabel. And there she was! Mother spotted her right away.

Willow Grove

Isabel Stricklin was my mother's surviving brother's oldest daughter. Her sister Emma was the youngest. Isabel, who never married, was a teacher and Emma, well, I don't know what she did, but she had two children around our age: Sandy and George Gaskins. When she saw us, Isabel greeted us warmly and took us to her car to drive us to Willow Grove, a small town about fifteen miles from Philadelphia. Willow Grove had an amusement park where my mother said that she had heard John Philip Sousa play when she was a girl. Like many people back then, my parents did not own a car, so riding in Isabel's car was a real treat. We had no busses to get on and off of and didn't then have to walk to our destination carrying heavy suitcases.

We drove through Philadelphia and out to Willow Grove, where Isabel lived in a big house next door to her father, my Uncle Carrol who lived with his white wife Ida. Emma lived with her children in a separate house on the same grounds. My uncle wasn't a farmer, but he owned quite a few acres of land, on which he grew vegetables and raised chickens. For added income, he worked odd jobs around town. Where they lived was so foreign to me. No busses going by on a regular basis like the one that passed our house on St. Ferdinand, not many cars on the roads either, and certainly no sidewalks. No people just walking by. We were out in the country. The air smelled sweet, there were strange birds, plants and flowers I had never seen before, and grass just growing where it wanted to, yet it all seemed so right to me, a city girl. Also, because there were so few colored people, we were in an integrated community and no one seemed to care. I immediately felt the difference between the segregated Ville and where I now was.

After greeting Aunt Ida, we got out of our traveling clothes and into our play clothes as fast as we could. My sister and I quickly found Sandy and George. The four of us were inseparable for the entire time we stayed in Willow Grove. They showed us creeks full of fish and flowers that I had never seen growing along the banks. We waded in the water in our tennis shoes, and tried to catch dragonflies. The flowers we picked quickly wilted, but that didn't matter. One day I wore a skirted swim suit that I thought was so pretty — it had flowers all over it

—and I thought that I looked so good in it. As we played with a hose in the garden, we screamed and laughed and ran and skipped with a freedom that I hardly ever felt in St. Louis. Was it because we were away from St. Louis and my father, or was it because everything was just so new to me?

After about four days we said a sad good-bye to everyone there and we were off next to Chestertown, Md.

Chestertown

Isabel drove us back to the train station where we boarded one that would take us to Elkton, Maryland. When we arrived in Elkton, my Uncle Ben would pick us up and drive us to Chestertown.

We wore the same garments that we had worn on the train from St. Louis to the Thirtieth Street Station, although our hair did not look quite as nice as it had when we left St. Louis.

We got on the train and when we got to the Elkton Station, Uncle Ben was waiting for us. We put our suitcases in the trunk and then piled into his 1947 Ford.

Mother sat in the front with him, and my sister and I sat in the back seat. He asked about our trip so far—the train from St. Louis and our stay in Willow Grove. We all tried to talk at once, telling him about all of the new things that we had seen and experienced.

He and Mother talked, and once or twice I heard them talk about the ferry, only I thought they were saying 'fairy.' We had to cross the bay on a fairy—a fairy? I imagined a fairy like I had seen in books, pale-skinned, with long, flowing, blond hair, a filmy dress and gossamer wings. I imagined that she would take each car and toss it from one side of the bay to the other, where it would gently land. I was terrified, although no one else seemed the least bit concerned.

Well, of course, when we got to the crossing, there was no fairy. The ferry was just a big boat that served as the bridge from one side of the Elk River to the other. I was both disappointed and greatly relieved.

We got out of the car as it was crossing the water. My mother and uncle chatted, while my sister and I ventured to stand next to the rail. It was new and wonderful time.

When we arrived at 210 West Calvert Street, Aunt Irene came out to greet us.

210 West Calvert St.

She was wearing a pinkish, soft cotton dress and high-heeled shoes. She had pretty legs which were her pride. She bragged about them to anyone who would listen. She also had beautiful white hair which framed her lovely face. The only thing that was not quite right was that she had lost all of her teeth. I guessed that was because of poor dental care, but she didn't let that stop her from being who I like to refer to as my elegant aunt.

We all piled out of the Ford, pulled our luggage out of the trunk and took all of our other stuff up stairs to our assigned rooms. Mother and my sister had the back room with twin beds, and I stayed in what I came to call "my room." It was the one that I occupied every time I visited Chestertown.

My uncle Ben & aunt Irene

The 210 West Calvert house had changed over the time since Aunt Irene and Uncle Ben bought it. Back then, it had an outhouse—clearly something that we didn't have in St, Louis.

Over the course of several years, some upgrades had made it quite a lovely home. I was delighted when one summer I found that it finally had an indoor toilet with a tub. The back bedroom and a sun room below had been added. The kitchen was small but adequate, and it got very hot when cooking in the summer.

My Aunt had furnished the house very nicely and had beautiful Persian rugs on hardwood floors. There was a front door that led out to the street, a side door that led to the side yard, and a back yard with large trees.

Calvert Street was busy, but not nearly as busy as St. Ferdinand in St. Louis. When people drove by, they always wiggled four of their fingers off the steering wheel, in what I though was kinda a peculiar greeting. But, no matter how many times in a day they might drive by, there was always that raised four fingers off the steering wheel wave.

Chestertown is an old, old small town, founded in 1706 on the Eastern Shore of Maryland. Its long history included a legend that George Washington had slept there. And because it was a Southern city, segregation prevailed in most aspects of daily living. Separate schools, colored housing apart from white housing, and of course separate churches—not unlike what I was accustomed to in St. Louis. This small town, on the Chester River, was surrounded by farms. It is known for the beautiful waterfront houses and colonial housing on or near High Street in town. People come from afar to see them. These details contributed to our love for the town, but, what was most important to me, even with its segregated way of life, was that we were away from St. Louis.

Freddie and I were lucky to have other kids, Brontea and Jesse our age to play with. They lived next door to my Aunt and Uncle. We would play out in front of the house in the street, or on the swing my uncle made for us in the garage, or run down the hill into a little woods behind the house. We could walk anywhere in town, and we did.

When it rained, there would be thunder and lightning unlike what we heard in St. Louis. The loud, crackling sound of the thunder and the flashing light seemed wonderful and so different from what I heard at home—and more than just a little bit frightening. We wore old shorts and blouses and tennis shoes. Our hair was mostly a mess, but no one seemed to care.

Sundays were the only days we had to dress up to go to church. On Sundays, we went to Janes United Methodist Church for Sunday school and church services. This church was not at all like the Episcopal Church we went to in St. Louis. The Episcopal service is liturgically-based, and services were done according to an ecclesiastical calendar. Those services had a rigid format, guided by the *Book of Common Prayer*. The church service at Janes United

Methodist Church had a different order to it, and seemed to me more free-form than the church services I was used to.

Just as I liked being away from my father, I liked being away from my St. Louis church. Not so restricted. I liked going to Janes because of that. The people who attended the church also did not seem as stiff and certainly not as uppity as the ones at home. Because we were Miss "Orene's" nieces (the local way of pronouncing her name) we seemed to be treated in a way that made us feel special.

After about a week of being in Chestertown, one day I decided to turn right, rather than left, when I left the house for a walk. Don't ask me why. I started walking toward the college. The college—Washington College—was the first college in the country to receive certification and was named for...yes, you guessed it, George Washington.

While Washington College was a prominent institution in the town, it was pretty much off limits to the colored people in town. Well yes, Blacks worked there as maids, gardeners, maintenance men and women, cooks and the like, but the college was really off limits to those Blacks who did not work there.

To decide to walk toward it was an unusual choice. Washington College was not a part of my world, my aunt's world, my uncle's world, or any colored person's world that I knew. To them, Washington College could have been on another planet.

Nevertheless, that morning I strolled up to the college and walked around, admiring the buildings and the landscaping. My mother had told me that her family, the Stricklins, had sold some property to the college, because the college wanted to expand.

I was wearing my usual shorts with a blouse and some sandals, and I was just taking in the sights. My Aunt Irene's house looked as nice as those nearest the college, so I didn't feel like I was in alien territory. I might have I been walking near those grand houses on the waterfront. They, like the houses near Washington College, were clearly located in the white part of town. I was just looking and taking in what I saw: Green lawns, flowers growing along the drives and under windows, and lawn chairs. I saw a young, white woman tending to her plants in the front yard. I raised my hand in greeting, said, "Hello" and she raised hers.

Washington College

After mother's family sold the property, my mother saved her share of the proceeds. Years later she used some of it to send me to college.

The undergraduate college I attended was not Washington College. No surprise there. No one I knew ever believed that any of us could go there.

My oldest sister, Betty Jane, went to the University of Maryland, College Park and NYU. Frederica, my baby sister, went to Bradley University in Peoria, Ill and the University of Illinois in Chicago.

I went to The University of Missouri, Columbia, Mo, UCLA, and ended up at The University of Southern California, where I got my doctoral degree.

I had just stopped and said hello to a young white woman. For a moment, she seemed a little surprised (me, a young Black girl speaking to a white adult?), but then she smiled and said, "Hello" to me.

I said, "Hi" in answer to her and walked on. My greeting her was, I think, just a part of who I was. While not on intimate terms with white people in St. Louis, I was not afraid of them, so saying 'hi' to her was just part of who I was. Not afraid.

I walked onto the Washington College campus, peeped into some buildings; saw a man cutting the lawn. I saw students entering and leaving buildings and saw one class being held under some shade trees. I tried to find the location of the weeping willow that the college had promised not to remove when they bought the house and land where my mother had been born and raised. But I don't think that the college kept its promise. I saw no tree that looked like a weeping willow anywhere. I gave up looking for it and started back to my aunt's house, I passed the lady I had seen earlier. Again, I said 'hi' to her and she smiled at me. Then she called out to me, "Little girl, would you like to stop a moment and have some lemonade?"

"What did you say, ma'am?" I responded in surprise. (Me, a young Black girl speaking to a white adult?)

"I said, would you like to sit with me here and have some lemonade?"

Well, this certainly was interesting. Out of nowhere, this strange, young white woman was asking this little colored girl—me—to have a glass of lemonade with her.

Several things immediately went through my mind: Is she crazy? Would I get into trouble? Is the lemonade poisoned and once dead, would I be buried under her rose bushes? Why is she asking me? Would I be kidnapped, never to be seen again? What would my Aunt Irene say if she knew I was sitting on some white lady's front lawn drinking lemonade?

But, in spite of those thoughts, I didn't let even one of those concerns stop me for a moment. I said, "Yes ma'am, I would. Thank you." She then invited me to sit on a lawn chair, went to get two glasses of lemonade, and then sat in the other chair facing me.

In a way, even though this was Maryland and the South, I was not afraid. Besides, Aunt Irene's house was just down the street. I think that, somehow, I was also just that secure in myself.

"Well," she said, "This is some good lemonade, if I do say so myself." She sipped the lemonade and smiled.

"So," she said, "tell me who you are."

"My name is Pauline Estelle, I am from St. Louis, and I am the niece of Mr. and Mrs. Graham. I, and my sister and mother, are visiting Chestertown for four weeks. I have been here two weeks already." I stopped, took a sip of lemonade and waited. I had said all of that really fast, and I needed to catch my breath.

"Mr. and Mrs. Graham?"

"Yes ma'am. They are both teachers. My aunt teaches here in Chestertown and has, I think, for a very long time, and my Uncle Ben teaches in Easton. Oh, and my father is also a teacher."

"You don't say," she said, "all of those teachers in your family? How interesting. I never thought that there could be so many colored teachers in one family."

"Oh, and my cousin in Philadelphia." I added. "She's a teacher, too."

She sat quietly for a moment and then said, "I am Mrs. Henry."

"And I told you that my name is Pauline Estelle. Pauline Estelle Merry."

We both said in unison, "Pleased to meet you," and we laughed.

She was wearing a white, soft cotton dress; her blond hair was streaked with white, and it came to her shoulders. As usual, I wore my hair in braids and, as usual, I was in my uniform of shorts, white top, and tennis shoes.

After finishing my lemonade, I thanked her and said that I should be getting back. She said, "Will you stop by tomorrow, Pauline Estelle?"

Without thinking, I said, "Sure, but it might be in the afternoon tomorrow, because my aunt said that she had something planned for us to do in the morning."

"Alright then," she said, "it's a date. I'll see you tomorrow afternoon."

The next morning, Aunt Irene and Uncle Ben took my mother, my sister, Aunt Carrie and me out to visit some people that my Aunt said were related to us. It seemed that everyone we met was some sort of cousin, since she often said this about people we met. I could never decide if they were really related to us, or if it was just a polite Southern way of relating to others. The cousins we were visiting had Stricklyn as their last name—not quite the same as my mother's maiden name, Stricklin. But they were close, so they were probably related to us.

To help end my confusion, we were told that the different spellings came about so that the mail wouldn't get mixed up between the two families. Aunt Irene wanted us to meet them, so that we would know more of our family members. I sorta had my nose in the air—they seemed too country for me, the fancy city girl. But, once I saw it, I loved where they lived, out in the country on a small farm. They had pigs and chickens and raised their own vegetables. Uncle Charles called to the pigs, but the pigs, not knowing me, refused to come to the troughs. So Uncle Charles asked me to stand behind him while he called them. They were big and not as smelly as I had expected. They jostled each other as they tried to get their big snouts in the trough for food. I reached out to touch one and to my surprise, it was rough and hairy, not what I had expected at all.

The farm house was not too large, but it was pretty with white curtains at the windows that sparkled in the sunshine. It had a large porch that went across the front. Uncle Charles said that they sometimes slept on it during hot, summer nights.

After being shown about the house and farm and drinking lemonade, we went home loaded down with tomatoes as big as my head, cucumbers, lettuce and fresh eggs. Uncle Charles told my aunt that come September or October he would bring her some pork chops from the fall slaughter. We thanked them for the food and bid them good-bye.

Driving along the country roads was so very different than driving in the city. Things seemed slower and more polite. Seeing the farm fields stretching to forever and the white clouds in the blue sky made me want to just stay and cuddle up somewhere with a good book. It was so different from St. Louis.

After we returned to my Aunt's house and had lunch, I excused myself, saying that I was just going for a short walk. No one questioned me about my destination; I hardly think they thought that I even had one. I was headed back to see Mrs. Henry as I had promised.

As I expected, Mrs. Henry was waiting for me. I had changed from the shorts I had worn to the farm to a white summer dress with flowers on it. She was wearing light blue pedal pushers and white blouse. She offered me some lemonade, which I happily accepted.

"How was your morning?" she asked.

I told her about our trip to my relatives' farm and how much I had enjoyed it. I told her that when I stood next to Uncle Charles when he called the pigs, the pigs, not knowing who I was, had refused to come to the pen. When I stood behind him so the pigs couldn't see me, they came hungrily to their food. After that I got to touch a pig—it was hairy! I had never in my life been that close to a pig.

Mrs. Henry laughed when I said that.

We sat quietly for a bit as I drank my lemonade, then she said to me, "Pauline Estelle, I have not been around many colored people at all, and I'd like to get to know more about you and your family. Oh, I see them about, but I've never...."

She stopped talking and I waited for her to go on.

She said, "This may seem odd to you, a grown white woman talking to a little colored girl, about wanting to know more about...well...her."

"What do you want to know?" I asked politely.

She went on, saying, "Don't you think it a bit odd that I would want to know about you?"

I sat a bit, thinking about her question. Finally I said, "Frankly, I hadn't thought about it before now."

"Oh," she said, seeming to be a little disappointed in my response. She went on to say, "You see, when you told me about all of the teachers in your family, I said to myself, 'Maude, you went to college and your husband teaches here in Chestertown at Washington College, yet you are really ignorant about some things right under your nose—like you really don't know much about colored people at all.' "

"How long have you lived in Chestertown?" I asked, somehow sensing that she hadn't been here long and maybe was a little lonely.

"We've been here...well, let me think...we've been here...well, my husband will begin his second year teaching at the college this coming fall, so I...we...have been here... just about a year."

I was right, she hadn't been here long. Then I asked if she and her husband had any kids.

"Not yet," she said, "but we are hoping to."

"Okay," I said again, "What else would you like to know?"

"Tell me, well, just tell me more about your family."

I opened my mouth to start telling her some things, when it dawned on me that I had been at her house for a while. So I said, "I think maybe I could start telling you about us tomorrow, if that's okay. I think that I should get back now."

She looked a little sad when I said that, but then she smiled and said, "What time tomorrow?"

"How about the same time as I came to day, after lunch?"

She said, "Great, I'll see you tomorrow, Pauline Estelle."

I said good-bye and headed home.

After dinner, my Aunt Irene, Mother, sister and I played Canasta with Aunt Fanny. Aunt Fanny wasn't actually related to us, but rather than address her as Mrs. Turner, she allowed us to call her Aunt. Now addressing a Black woman as "Aunt" was often a means by which white people would not acknowledge the proper status of a Black woman, so rather than calling her Mrs. This or Miss That, they would say "Aunt."

I also had learned that my grandparents had been "honored" in such a manner by having the two rooms set aside for Black people in the small local hospital labeled "Aunt Isabel" and "Uncle Josiah." My Aunt Irene was not the least bit happy with that designation, but was not able to do anything about it. Remember, this was Maryland. I heard sometime later that a young white boy had been admonished by his mother for addressing a Black man as Mr. so and so. His mother said to him, "You can't address Black people as Mr. or Mrs. It's not the thing to do. It will give them airs."

Some Black folks retaliated by giving a child the first name "Miss" or "Sir," to force white folks to call them by titles that they would otherwise not use. A rather clever way for those parents to get at least the appearance of respect for their children.

We played Canasta on a card table that had been set up in her back yard. A gate between Aunt Fanny's backyard and Aunt Irene's had been put in to allow for easy access, which was a neighborly gesture and which made us feel closer to her and her husband.

They had a dog named Angel. Angel would lie down in the middle of the road in front of the house and nap—that's how little traffic went up and down Calvert Street. Anyway, we played many rounds of Canasta, for many evenings. It was a pleasant activity involving other people. At home in St.

Louis, we rarely had people over and so to be with others outside my own family was a delicious treat.

That evening, while playing cards, I told my Aunt Irene, Aunt Fanny and mother about having visited Mrs. Henry. The three of them looked at me questioningly—with eyebrows raised. One of them said, "You visited with the white lady? What was her name? Oh, I remember, Mrs. Henry, on her front lawn up near the college?"

I said. "Yes, she invited me to sit with her and she gave me a glass of lemonade. Did I do something wrong?"

The grownups looked at each other for a moment, and then Aunt Fanny said, "Well, it's kinda unusual for white folks to entertain colored folks here, especially little girls, on their front lawn. But no, you didn't do anything wrong."

I told them that Mrs. Henry said that she was relatively new to the town, that her husband taught at the college, and that she had asked me to come back and visit her again.

They looked at one another, and they agreed that it would be okay for me to visit her, but that I should be careful. Careful of what they didn't say, but I agreed that I would be. I felt a little relieved that I had told them about my plans for future visits. It made the past and any future visits that I might have with Mrs. Henry okay.

On subsequent visits with Mrs. Henry, she told me about herself, her husband and why they had come to Chestertown. He had finished his master's degree in philosophy and wanted to teach at the college, as he had visited Chestertown as a youth and liked it here. She didn't know anything about Chestertown, but when presented with the opportunity to move to a historic town with her husband, and that he would be a professor there, she agreed that they should come.

Both of their families lived on the East coast, so visiting each other's family would not be too much of an inconvenience for either side of the family. She had graduated from Vassar. (I remembered hearing this name, and being told it was one of the "Seven Sisters" colleges—a famous group of colleges for women, and I had heard of Vassar as where the niece of my father's first wife had graduated.). But even with a college degree, Mrs. Henry had no career aspirations.

After telling me about herself, she wanted to know how it came to be that there were so many teachers in my family. "Well," I said, "they went to college, of course." She looked surprised, and asked "Washington College?"

I looked at her as though she was a little "tetched in the head," as my father would say. "Not quite right." There was never any question that my sister and I would go to some college, but not once did I hear it suggested that we would go to Washington College. Not once. Except for the land that the family had sold to the college, it was never a part of my family's lives. And although Black folks worked there as maids, cooks, cleaning people and the like, narry a Black student was to be seen.

Washington College didn't have a Black graduate until 1962, exactly 180 years after it had been established—180 years!

I felt like she was genuinely interested in me and my family—and not in an unkind way.

Probably she wanted to know about colored folks in general. And since she had me to talk to, it seemed that I was educating her about Black folks. Well, to be clear, I was telling her about my family who, I suppose, were in part representative of Black folk. At least to her. But even I knew about generalities and what that meant. There is no One Size Fits All when it comes to people. No two people fit the same mold.

I got into the habit of visiting Mrs. Henry almost every day. We sat on her front lawn drinking iced tea or lemonade that I believed she made especially for me. One day, she asked me if I knew anything about where my family had come from. How they had gotten to Chestertown? I told her that I didn't know, but that I would try and find out.

That evening I asked Aunt Irene, "How did the Stricklins get to Chestertown, and when and why?"

She looked at me and my mother (her baby sister) and said, "Well you know, I am not really sure how they got here. Do you know, Pauline?"

"No, I have no idea?"

"Then does Aunt Carrie know?" I asked.

Well it turns out that no one, neither my aunts nor my mother knew much about how it had come to pass that the Stricklins were in Chestertown.

When I told this to Mrs. Henry, she said to me, "Well, I think that we might have a project. Would you like to learn a little about your family's history?"

I thought a moment...and then I thought, why not? The idea that my family even had a history had never occurred to me.

I said to her, "I think that we should get permission from my aunts and my mother," not really knowing what learning about the history of my family meant.

Mrs. Henry said, "Well, of course. We should ask them permission to do a little research."

"All right," I said. But inside my head, I had to figure out just how we would get that permission. White people didn't visit colored people, at least I had never seen that happen, either in St. Louis or here.

And Black people didn't visit white people's homes. The only time they went to them was as maids or cooks, and at that they came through the back door, certainly not as a visitor, as far as I could tell.

Finally, I figured that the only thing to do was to ask my Aunt Irene.

That evening after dinner and several rounds of Canasta, I said, as casually as I could, "Aunt Irene, Mrs. Henry would like to come visit you and ask permission to do a little research on the Stricklin family with me." We were all outside, it was hot and we were all dressed in cool summer clothes drinking ice tea: Aunt Irene, my mother, Aunt Carrie, my sister, Uncle Ben, and Aunt Fannie.

The fireflies were doing their thing, crickets were singing to each other and the air smelled sweet. There was a hint of rain in the air. With my question, all of the grownups, holding glasses of iced tea half-way to their mouths, stopped and stared at me.

Oh, oh, I thought. What have I gone and said or done? I wasn't surprised at their immediate response, which was complete silence. I just didn't know what was going to follow. Would it be an outright no, or a maybe, or a what? Actually, I don't think that they knew what to say either.

"Well," my mother said, "tell us more."

I told them what I knew about Mrs. Henry and her husband, that I had been visiting her a lot, and that she seemed a bit lonely. I had not met her husband; I guess he was teaching, I didn't know for sure.

"And why does she want to do research on us?" my mother asked.

"I think it is because I told her about the number of teachers in our family and she was, as she said, "...surprised to know that there were so many teachers in one colored family.""

At that, they all laughed out loud. I don't remember who, but one of them said, "It's just like white folks to underestimate what colored folks can do. They seem to think that we have no brains, and that if it weren't for them, we'd

still be doing lord only knows what in the jungles of Africa–
not anything that required an education beyond the 8th
grade, if that, and certainly not anything professional. Sure,
let her do some research on this family. It might put some
sense in her head about who we are, and I don't just mean
our family, but colored folks in general!"

Then I quietly asked, "When can she come and ask you?"

Aunt Irene said, "How about this coming Sunday
afternoon, right in our living room. I bet she's never been in
a colored person's house in her entire life. Just let her come
and see how we live. I'll guarantee you she'll be quite
surprised."

My Uncle then said to the others, "Let's make her come to
the back door." They all laughed out loud, slapping their
knees.

I said that I would let Mrs. Henry know. And I asked,
"Will you really make her come to the back door?"

"Of course not," my Aunt said. "We were just laughing at
white folks for a change."

I had an experience of once being told to go to the back
door, when I was taking music lessons from Mrs. Murillo out
in Overland, Missouri. I was returning a double bass to her
and went to the front door of her house with it, only to be
told by some young white girl who answered the door to take
the instrument to the back door. I remember looking at her
in surprise, knowing she was asking me to do something that
wasn't right, but rather than tell her no, I took the
instrument to the back door anyway. It was a strange event
in my life. I'd never before been asked to go to anyone's back
door, but rather than challenge her, I did what she asked.
Perhaps I shouldn't have, but I did. Maybe I should have
just left the instrument on the front porch.

Now I had a quite a bit to think about. I was curious
about the response that the grown-ups had when I asked if
Mrs. Henry could come over. I really wanted to understand

the laughter and their resentment which, while not directly spoken, was nonetheless part of their reaction.

Having lived in the environment of second- class citizenship all of their lives, with separate schools and housing in places for colored only, my relatives were both bitter and amused that some white woman wanted to learn more about us and, consequently, more about the colored people she saw, but with whom she had little personal interaction.

America came to be the most powerful nation on Earth, in part because from very early in its founding it was built on two evils. The first one was the systematic genocide of Native Americans.

Starting in the early 1600s white colonizers stole the Native Americans' land right out from under them. They did that just because (with their guns) they could. Besides, they thought, these people look funny (their skin is so red) and they don't worship God the right way.

At first, the conquerors simply decided to kill all the pesky people who claimed a right to their historic lands. Then, in 1819 the leaders decided it would be less expensive to simply try to "convert" the children from their culture as Native Americans and make them into "proper" Americans (like themselves). To do this they set up Indian Schools all over the United States and they forced all the Native American children they could find to live, work, and study at these schools, forbidding them from speaking their Indian languages or spending time with their families —hoping that this would make them into proper Americans. This strategy continued until sometime in the 1960s.

You may not be surprised to learn that few of these Indian children appreciated this treatment. So the attempt to make the Native American cultures and Tribal governments go away quite simply failed.

All along the Native Americans thought they had perfectly good Tribal governments and rules for how to live life, so they weren't happy to have someone come along and tell them they were wrong. After much negotiation the United States agreed that the Native American had been organized into several different sovereign nations. So in 1869 the US government and the several separate Native American nations worked out some treaties explaining how they would relate to one another from then on. But still, the Indian School strategy persisted.

Unfortunately, the treaties between Native Americans and the US government have all-too-often been ignored. After taking away the Indians' lands, they were forced to live on 'reservations,' often created on the least desirable parts of their land, or somewhere far from where they were originally.

Many who live on those reservations still lack adequate water and electricity and are far from essential services like hospitals, schools and grocery stores. On the other hand, one benefit they do have is that every Native American living within the United States is also a US citizen, as well as a member of their Tribe.

On the next page is a poster created in 1976 (the 200th anniversary of our country's founding) to explain a common Native American's attitude toward the US government. Here is its caption:

Entitled the "Shrine of Hypocrisy," This poster shows the U.S. Mount Rushmore National Monument, joined by Sitting Bull surveying the scene. The Black Hills, where the monument is, were guaranteed to the Lakota people in the Fort Laramie Treaty of 1868 and as the quote by Old Joseph (Chief Joseph's father) says, **"always remember, your fathers never sold this land,"** (meaning that the U.S. Mount Rushmore National Monument is on stolen land).

(This image, was originally published in the Akwesasne Notes in 1976, is included here courtesy of the Akwesasne Notes/Indian Time Newspaper https://www.indiantime.net/, who now own the copyrights on all the Akwesasne Notes and the images therein.
The caption text is courtesy of the Center for the Study of Political Graphics https://www.politicalgraphics.org/)

"always remember - your fathers never sold this land"

The second evil the United States was built on was the enslavement of Africans who had been kidnapped and brought to America.

The European conquerors needed help transforming the land (that they had stolen) so, starting in 1619, they bought other human beings (now called "slaves") to do that hard work. That's right, they BOUGHT other humans from the slave traders, with the slaves having no say in the matter.

The people who ended up founding and running the United States believed that these humans (the slaves) didn't deserve any better treatment, again because they didn't look right (their skin was too brown or black) and they also didn't worship God the right way, at least at first. All of these slaves (a word to describe *their unfortunate status) had been free people in Africa until a slave trader captured them and brought them to the new country being built in America where they were then sold as slaves.*

These formerly free Africans, now US slaves, provided much of the labor to build cities in the North and pick cotton in the South, both activities that were huge drivers of the economic growth of the country.

On top of these evils were the enactment of laws that were beneficial to whites, but that extremely restricted the opportunities of both the Native Americans and the enslaved Africans to prosper—even after slavery, as such, had been outlawed in the United States in 1868 (by ratification of the 14th Amendment to the U.S. Constitution).

Since Blacks and Native Americans could not change their skin color, they continued to be discriminated against, whereas all the different groups of people who came to America from different parts of Europe and elsewhere eventually came to be called white. They were encouraged to abandon their birth identities, as Germans, Poles, Swedes, or Italians, for example, and after awhile, were seen as part of the dominant group that had the financial and political control of the country—a group simply called the whites.

The African slaves were human beings, just like their white masters. That meant that they could have children together. Some of today's African Americans are purely descendants of Africans; others have a mixture of white and Black ancestors. But all of them were considered by their society to be Blacks (or "coloreds") and thus not entitled to the privileges given to whites.

These white people made the laws that allowed them to prosper. They passed Jim Crow laws that created segregation, separate housing, and segregated schooling laws. These laws left little opportunity for non-whites to have jobs, decent housing, and good schooling—all the things that whites had come to expect.

The mass migration of colored people from the South to the North and the West was in response to the repressive laws and living conditions that governed their lives in the South. But, alas, the same repressive laws and cultural attitudes followed them north and west. Although not to the degree that existed in the South, these laws, and the white attitudes about Blacks, nevertheless, kept them as second-class citizens.

I learned the details of these social and political issues more fully later on. But even then, on some level, I understood my relatives' reaction that summer in Chestertown. After all, I was from St. Louis and not totally unaware of how segregation affected my life there.

So, it was arranged for Mrs. Henry to come to my aunt and uncle's house after church the following Sunday.

And, on the following Sunday, Mrs. Henry arrived.

My Aunt's home was immaculate; in fact it was from her that my sister and I learned how to clean a house. Our mother was not much of a housekeeper. Neat as our house was, I can't remember ever seeing my mother with a dust cloth or broom in her hands. Yet, I knew that Aunt Irene would worry that this white lady coming to her home would be critical of how it looked. Part of me wanted to reassure her that Mrs. Henry wouldn't care, but how was I even to know that. I just made the assumption that because Mrs. Henry had been nice to me, her generosity would extend to my aunt. In any event, it seemed that everyone was waiting to greet Mrs. Henry.

That Sunday after church, they were all there: Aunt Irene, Aunt Carrie, my Mother, my sister, Aunt Fanny and Uncle Ben. We were all just a tiny bit nervous. We were still wearing our Sunday church clothes and everyone looked really nice. Mrs. Henry, wearing a simple white cotton dress, came shyly into the room, sat on the chair that was offered her and repeated the names of everyone in the room.

We all smiled and said, "Glad to meet you."

She smiled back and began to tell everyone about herself and the project she had in mind. She said, "I was an American history major in college and I have always been interested in other people's lives." She smiled a little when she said this. "I would like to teach history at the college, but they said that they don't need another woman in the department. As my husband has a position in the philosophy department… well, they said that they couldn't use me, leaving me with little to do and, frankly, I am bored. I would like to put some of my training to use and learn about your family. When Pauline Estelle said that many members of your family were teachers, that got me interested in you. I thought that there is some interesting history I could learn about and that it might be of interest to you, and Pauline Estelle as well."

She seemed a bit breathless when she stopped.

No one sitting in our nicely-decorated room said anything as she spoke. The furniture shined, having been polished that morning. The curtains at the front window had been recently washed. The fine carpets had been swept. The antimacassars on the chairs and couch had been washed and starched. Some of my aunt's elephant collection had been carefully placed on two of the end tables, and someone had placed a vase of cut roses on the table in front of the couch.

Uncle Ben said, "What is the project you have in mind?"

She turned to him and said, "Well, Mr. Graham, I was thinking that Pauline Estelle and I would go down to the courthouse to see if we could find any family records on the Stricklins. From them, you would likely know more about your family history, at least on that side of the family."

Someone, I think it was Aunt Fanny, said, "Hmmm. Yes. I think that would be a very interesting thing to do. I know very little about my own family." Then she turned to Aunt Irene and said, "Reeney, what do you know about the Stricklins?" (Reeny is what our family and close friends called her.)

Aunt Irene turned to Aunt Carrie, who was the oldest of the three sisters and said, "Carrie, what do you know about our family?" It felt as though they had all but forgotten that Mrs. Henry was still there.

It seemed that no one knew anything but one or two pieces of stories about their grandfather, father and mother.

Then Mrs. Henry spoke up, "So there you are. No one here seems to know much about your family. So may I please have your permission to take Pauline Estelle to the old court building? We will research through the court's records to see what we can learn about you. It would give me a great honor to do that, it would also help me use my mind more, and who knows what we might find. The college might even reconsider and hire me as an instructor, if only part-time, that is, if my husband would let me."

Uncle Ben again spoke first, saying, "What do you have to do to look at the records? Do you need our permission to look at public records?" He paused, then added, "Well, of course you don't need permission. They are public records. But I guess what you want from us is our family's permission for you to explore our past." As he looked around the room, everyone smiled and nodded.

Permission had been granted.

Early the next morning, Mrs. Henry came by 210 West Calvert Street, knocked on the door, waited for me to join her. Off we went to the courthouse. She was wearing a different white summer dress. I was wearing my dark green shorts with a light green blouse and, of course, tennis shoes. My hair was a summer mess, but I didn't mind. In fact, I hardly missed having my hair straightened with a hot comb; it would just "go back," the description we used when our kinky hair resumed its natural state.

When Mrs. Henry picked me up it didn't seem that any of the neighbors were interested in what she and I were doing, but I could almost feel their eyes on my back as we made our way to the courthouse. After a few times of her picking me up, she and I decided that I would just meet her at the courthouse, because it was equidistant between my aunt's house and her's. Although, when she did pick me up, we had time to chat as we walked. When she stopped, I missed those short times we had together.

In about two weeks, I would be going back to St. Louis. She and I were unsure about how much we would get done before I left. When I mentioned that, she said, "I'll continue the work after you are gone, and I will send you the results at the same time I share them with your aunt and uncle." That made sense to me, and we proceeded with the search.

Going through over a hundred years of records took lots and lots of time. The records were dusty. We sat in a smallish room with long tables and because we were not always sure who we were looking for, the clerk brought us old record books and even gave us suggestions about what and whom to look for. We were not always sure what the individuals' names were. On occasion, after a morning's work, we would ask Aunt Irene or Aunt Carrie what they knew for sure, or remembered hearing about some of what we had discovered.

One story they told me was that there were two white brothers who essentially started the Stricklin family. One married a white woman. The other married a Black woman who was my mother's grandmother. Her daughter Isabel was the mother of Carrie, Carroll, Elijah, Irene and my mother, Pauline. The research that Mrs. Henry and I were doing would bear this out, but that was just a small part of our history.

Eventually, my last day, for that summer, to be in Chestertown, had come. I regretted having to stop my "research," being with my aunt and uncle, and—even more —I dreaded going back to St. Louis.

The night before we left, we enjoyed a delicious country dinner of oven-baked chicken, a specialty of Uncle Ben's, farm-fresh vegetables, sliced cucumbers, a favorite of Aunt Irene, and tall glasses of ice tea. We had our usual Canasta game after dinner, and we even invited Mrs. Henry to join us, but she declined.

I'd had a great time in Chestertown that summer and I was looking forward to coming back. Returning home to St. Louis, we reversed our steps: Uncle Ben, Aunt Irene with us this time driving back to Elkton, taking the ferry to Pennsylvania, where Isabel met us and took us to the Thirtieth Street train station. She brought Sandy and George along with her, giving us time to see them once again. While we were not allowed to play or run in the station, we were all happy to see each other even for those few moments.

On our train trip back to St. Louis, we had our own sleeping compartment. The seats converted into bunk beds that the porter made up for us, and we had our own private toilet and wash basin. We ate all of our meals in the dining car. Riding in our own compartment topped off the summer. I had had a great time in Chestertown, and I looked forward to going back there again.

More than six months later, I heard from Mrs. Henry. She wrote she had spent many more hours looking through old musty, dusty records and sent me this diagram showing my direct ancestors on my mother's side. She said she had also given a copy of it to my Aunt Irene, Aunt Carrie and Uncle Ben.

I looked through what she sent me. It seemed pretty skimpy for all of the time it took, including the time I had spent with her six months earlier, but here was something concrete about my mother's family. Of course my mother, who had been the first one to see the envelope, was curious. I immediately shared its contents with her. When my father arrived home, he looked at it as well. We all concluded that it was a good start.

Their history was something neither of my parents had ever considered looking for. I think in part it was because their ancestors had been enslaved, the family histories of most Black people were non-existent. It is as though those of us who survived being enslaved had to start from scratch to learn about who we were, individually, and as a people.

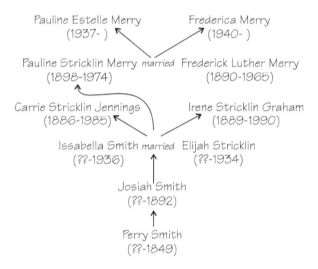

I wrote a letter to Mrs. Henry, thanking her for the time she and I had spent together on her front lawn and in the Hall of Records. And, of course, I thanked her for the history that she found and promised her that I would continue, sometime in the future, to look for more information about the Stricklins, and, if I could, some about my father's side of our family. I also said that I hoped she would continue her research about other Black families in Chestertown. And I hoped she would be offered a teaching position at Washington College because of her research. I even suggested that she not ask her husband for permission to take a position if she was offered one!

* * * * *

Some Questions to Think About

1. Have you ever ridden on a train? If yes, where did you go? Have you ever traveled by airplane? If yes, where to?

2. Have you ever traveled to visit relatives who lived far from you? If you have, what was interesting and fun about that trip? If you haven't, who would you like to visit? (It could even be someone you don't know yet!)

3. What do you think makes traveling to other places fun? What might make it scary?

4. Many different languages are spoken and written around the world. If you traveled somewhere where everyone spoke a different language from your own, would that matter to you? Why would it matter? What other differences might also matter as you travel?

5. Have you ever traveled to somewhere all by yourself? If 'yes,' where did you go, and why? How did you travel — by bus? Train? Other? If 'no,' where can you imagine yourself going alone?

6. Describe one new place that you have visited. How was it the same and how was it different from where you live?

7. Have you ever talked with your grandparents, or any siblings of your parents, about where they came from? And how they came to be where they are now?

8. What do you know about your Family History?

9. Some people describe other people by their race or ethnicity. What do you understand those word, "race" and "ethnicity" mean?

10. Is your race or ethnicity important to you? Why or why not?

If You Want to Learn More
Here are two good sources of information:

The Pullman Porters were both commonplace and of vital importance to the train travelers, both while and Black. You can learn more about their history here: https://www.cntraveler.com/story/pullman-porters-train-legacy

Christopher Cathcart ed, HBCU Experience - The Book: A Collection of Essays Celebrating the Black College Experience Paperback – August 6, 2014 by Tyree

I'd love to hear from you, my readers.
You may contact me, the author, by emailing
me at:
PaulineEstelleMerry@GreatTalesToldWell.com

Map: "My World"

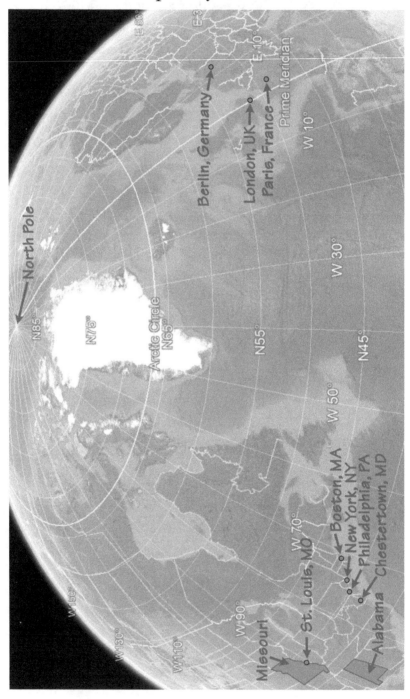

Story 5
Sumner High School

After graduating from Cote Brilliante Elementary School, in 1950, I went to Sumner High School, one of the three public high schools in St. Louis that Black kids could attend. As I had little choice in where I would go, I knew that going there would be a challenge, because I was thirteen, had chocolate-colored skin, was skinny, had nappy hair, pimply skin and a host of other characteristics that, to me, were not the best things to be or have if I were to be happy there. On top of that, my father taught at the high school. Who in her right mind would want a parent in a place where she was trying to be herself? Tell me who? Right, no one!

My father was totally unsympathetic to my concerns. He often said to me that what mattered wasn't how I looked—instead what mattered was what was inside my head.

I was entering a whole new world in which I would have to learn how to navigate it so that I could be in control of my experiences—at least, as best I could. Civil rights activism turned out to be my way through the challenges of going to Charles Sumner High School. That I went to a school named after an abolitionist was, in a way, providential.

While I was a student there, I didn't think too much about the history or importance of Sumner High School. Later on I learned that it was the oldest Black High School west of the Mississippi River, founded in 1875, and moved in 1909 to its present location. It was named for Charles Sumner, a distinguished United States Senator from Massachusetts who was an ardent abolitionist (someone opposed to anyone being made a slave). On May 22, 1856, He was beaten unconscious by an ardent advocate of slavery. (See a link at the end of this story.)

On my first day of high school, my father had left for work early. I followed him about an hour later, walking from Hammett Place to our school. I was excited but also felt some fear. I had lived behind Sumner on St. Ferdinand the first eleven years of my

Sumner High School

life and I had been in the building on several occasions. This was my first day as a student there. I would know some of the kids who had also attended Cote Brilliante School, and maybe see some of the others from my years at Simmons, like Betty and Shirley. But being a student at the high school was new, really new.

Freshmen were directed to the auditorium. I walked to the middle of the auditorium, waved to some kids that I knew and took a seat. Mr. Brantley, the long-time principal, welcomed us. Then he introduced some of the administrators and teachers that we would come to know. Next, out of nowhere, he said, "Is Pauline Estelle Merry here?" I looked around and then stood up, wondering why he had called on me.

"Please come to the stage."

I was wearing a new maroon plaid pleated skirt and a white blouse and sweater – Sumner High's colors. My hair had just been pressed and curled the day before, so I knew that I looked okay, but I was really nervous. Mr. Brantley said, "I understand that you play the piano well. Please play something for us."

Well, I was in shock, and at a total loss. I had not been told that he would call on me. I had not prepared anything to play. Someone brought out some music for me—I think it might have been the Black National Anthem, "Lift Every Voice and Sing." Not something I had ever played before. I sat down and tried to sight read the music—which was not one of my strong suits—still I struggled and played it, as well as I could. Finally, I left the stage and, along with all of the other freshmen, we were excused to our respective homerooms.

As I was going down the stairs, I heard some teacher snidely remark to my father, "Merry, how about that performance?" My father was extremely embarrassed, and so was I. I don't recall that he said anything about it at home, but I knew he had been supremely hurt by his colleague's sarcastic statement and also hurt by having been embarrassed in front of them by me. I never again played a piano at Sumner. Never.

Mr. Jackson was my new homeroom teacher, I recognized one or two students I had known from Simmons and Cote Brilliante. Along with them, I received my schedule of classes. It was pretty daunting – Latin, English, Algebra, US history and PE. I did not do super well in any of my classes except English and PE. Having taken those tough classes in my freshman year, I struggled for the next three years to bring up my overall grade point average. I wanted to qualify for The National Honor Society, but in the end I failed to do this, which was, I knew, an enormous disappointment for my father.

I was insecure in every fiber of my being. Here I was, a dark-skinned, nappy-haired, skinny girl who was the daughter of one of the hardest teachers in the school. As I walked down the hall, I would hear whispers: "There goes Mr. Merry's daughter." That was no fun at all. And, of course, all of the teachers knew who I was.

When I was a student at Sumner, indirectly, I had to deal with the unknown elements of the faculty politics. Teachers and school administrators alike had to deal with their own social and political needs, for their personal and professional growth and survival. But of course, I knew nothing about all that.

Sumner High School Faculty Event 1954

Frederick Luther Merry

I knew that my father failed to get a promotion that he wanted. Years later, as I ascended the ladder as a college administrator myself, I came to know first-hand about faculty and administrator politics, and how vicious they could be.

Meanwhile I had to deal with my "here and now." I had to figure out a way to survive Sumner for the next four years. It wasn't just about simple survival. I wanted to be *me* in a way that would make me feel good about who I was. And in order to do that, I had to take stock of the things that made me *me*.

I usually walked to school alone; my father always went to school before I did, and my sister went in the opposite direction to her elementary school. I treasured that time I had to myself. It gave me time to think and dream. I had to walk about seven, fairly long blocks, from my house on Hammett Place to Sumner. I enjoyed the change of seasons in the Midwest: falling leaves in autumn, ice and snow in the winter, trees budding with new leaves in the spring. I walked past two-family flats, small single dwellings, four-family flats. There were well-kept houses, brick ones, ones that needed repair, mowed lawns with flowers under front windows, and some front yards with dogs tied up to a tree and with little to no grass.

What I wore, depended on the season, of course. Heavy coats, warm jackets, sweaters and sweater sets. Blouses with peter-pan collars. Saddle shoes and penny loafers. My skirts came well below my knees, and I never wore pants—except on weekends, when blue jeans or peddle-pushers were the accepted attire.

As I walked, I would think: How am I going to get through going to Sumner on my own terms? I didn't want to be fearful. I wanted to be successful, not really knowing what success meant. I just knew that on some level, I wanted to be in charge of myself and understand the challenges, as well as the opportunities, that existed. I may not have used those exact words, but there was a striving deep inside me that I wanted to honor.

I made a list of my strengths and weaknesses and then of my needs. What did I want? How did I want to be in the world? I didn't know how to do all that. I just knew that my survival depended on figuring it out.

Underlying these thoughts was that I knew that my family was different. We didn't socialize much at all with others. My parents had no relatives nearby. My father's sister lived in Los Angeles, and I saw her only once as I was growing up. My wonderful mother's two dear sisters lived a thousand miles away in Chestertown, Maryland, and we only saw them in summers. My mother's brother, Carroll lived in Willow Grove, Pennsylvania with his family, and I saw them only once growing up.

And further, my mother had no friends—none. My father's friends seldom came to our house, except for the male teachers with whom he played chess and bridge. So we were very much an isolated, nuclear family, alone and on our own. I also knew that while we didn't have a lot of money— actually no one we knew did—our social status was relatively high. I think this was largely because both of my parents were college-educated, which was a very rare thing for many adults, and even more so for colored people.

Yet, in spite of these issues, which were more like background noise—and even though, here I was, just a skinny, little brown skinned, nappy headed girl—how was I going to survive Sumner? What could I do that was special? What could I do that was different?

Racism in this country (something that I didn't learn about until much later) prohibited most colored people from advancing beyond being laborers and maids and the like.

There were "Jim Crow laws" (laws that restricted what colored people could do), and real estate companies "red-lined" areas, marking the only areas where coloreds could buy homes, were the rule and not the exception. Colored GIs home from World War II were denied educational advancement because they did not have access to the GI Bill. Over 100,000 Black soldiers were denied the GI Bill. Whites kept us back, kept us struggling, kept us poor, kept us subject to illnesses, because there was little health care available.

But as a thirteen year old, I really didn't know any of this, I just lived my life as best I could, and my parents provided for me and my sister as best they could—as did most parents in those post-WW2 years.

As I was walking to school one day, passing by one of the smaller, well-cared-for houses on St. Ferdinand, just west of Taylor Avenue, an older, gray-haired lady, came out to the gate of the wood fence that surrounded her house.

It was in late September, beginning to really feel like fall. I was wearing a green plaid skirt, a white blouse, and a lighter green sweater. My short, black hair was pressed, and I had bangs. I also had pimples on my forehead, something that really bothered me, but there was little could I do about them, except apply skin creams that did absolutely no good to stop them from appearing. I tried hiding them with make-up and praying that in twenty years I wouldn't have them, but anyway, there I was as I was. I smiled and spoke to the lady, "Good morning ma'am."

"Good morning, little girl. On your way to school?" she asked.

"Yes, ma'am, I am."

"Well, good for you. What grade are you in?" she asked.

"Ninth grade, ma'am," I replied.

"Well, you have a good day at school." she said.

"Yes, ma'am, I will. Thank you."

And I went on to school.

The next day, the lady was at her gate, wearing a plain grey cotton dress with red buttons down to the waist. Her hair was in a long braid tied with a matching red ribbon. It seemed as though she was waiting for me to pass by.

"Good morning, little girl, on your way to school?" she asked.

"Yes ma'am, I am." She smiled and said that she hoped that I would have a good day at school.

The next morning she wasn't there, but she was the next, and she again said, "Good morning, little girl, on your way to school?" and I said, "Yes ma'am, I am." And then she asked me my name. "It's Pauline Estelle," I said.

"Oh, what a nice, melodic name you have." Melodic? No one had ever said that about my name. I wasn't even sure I knew what it meant, but it seemed nice and a bit unusual. So I asked her, "Ma'am, what do you mean...melodic?"

She smiled and said, "It has a sense of music about it. Say it— Pauline Estelle, Pauline Estelle, Pauline Estelle. Doesn't it sound a bit like a song to you?"

Well, of course, I had never thought about my name sounding like music before but it was a very nice idea. It seemed special somehow.

She then said, "Think about it a bit. You'll begin to hear music when you hear your name called."

"Well, thank you very much," I said to her and continued walking on to school. But, that day, as I was walking to and then back home after school, I thought about what she had said. I hoped that I would see her the next day, and I did.

"Good morning ma'am," I said, smiling when I saw her. "I am glad to see you. I was afraid that you might not be at your gate when I walked by."

"Well, Pauline Estelle," she said, "here I am, and I am glad to see you as well. How's the girl with the melodic name this morning? "

"I am doing fine, ma'am, thank you. How are you this morning? And may I ask you your name? It seems rude of me not to know it."

She smiled and said, "Well, Pauline Estelle, my name is Mrs. Agnes Burroughs. And by the way, what is your last name, since you now know mine?"

"Nice to meet you, Mrs. Burroughs. My last name is Merry."

"Merry," she exclaimed. "I knew a Frederick Merry. Could he be related to you? It is an unusual name. And furthermore, that name adds to the melodiousness of your name—Pauline Estelle Merry."

I laughed out loud and said, "My father is Frederick Merry, he's a teacher. Could he be the man you knew?"

"Well, lord have mercy! Yes, perhaps he is the Frederick Merry I knew. We used to call him Freddie. Where is he and what is he doing?" she asked.

"He teaches at Sumner and I'd love to tell you more," I said, "but I am sorry Mrs. Burroughs, I have to go. Unless I leave now, I will be late for school."

She said, "Oh, my goodness, girl, you get going. We can talk again. This is so exciting. I will look for you tomorrow."

In parting I said, "Tomorrow is Saturday, and I won't be coming this way, but perhaps I will see you on Monday. I hope so."

"I hope so, too," she said with a smile. "I'll be looking for you."

On Saturday, I went to my piano lessons out in Overland. Sunday was church at All Saints Episcopal Church. I suppose that I did some studying over the weekend, but I can't remember having done much.

The following Monday, as I passed Mrs. Burroughs' little house, she wasn't there. Nor was she there the next day or the entire week. I gave some thought about her absence, but it never occurred for me to knock on her door. I slowed down as I passed, but I never stopped. So the week passed.

The next week, I left my house a little earlier than usual, hoping that I would see her. As I walked a little faster toward her house, I craned my neck forward to get an early glance—and there she was. I ran toward her, yelling as I ran. "Hi, Mrs. Burroughs. There you are! Where have you been?"

She said, "Good morning, Pauline Estelle. I am glad to see you as well. I didn't have a chance to tell you that I wouldn't be home last week, and I wondered how I could get a message to you. You'll have to give me your phone number and address. If this ever happens again, then I can call your house, or send you a note."

Well, I wasn't so sure that I wanted her sending me a letter, or calling my house. I didn't want my parents to tell me I couldn't spend time with Mrs. Burroughs. So I said, "Perhaps you can stick an envelope in your screen door, with my name printed on it in big letters. If I didn't see you at the gate, I'll know to look at the screen to see if there is an envelope with my name on it waiting for me."

She agreed that would be a good idea. But having spent a while with her, I realized that if I spent any more time, I'd be late for school. I suggested that I come, maybe around 8:15 a.m. the next morning so that we could chat and I wouldn't be late for school. She agreed to that as well. So off I ran, saying, "I'll see you tomorrow."

The next morning I arrived at her gate at 8:15. My mother didn't question why I was leaving a bit early. Had she asked, I would have just said that I had to meet my friend, Valena, early for a project we were working on.

"Good morning, Mrs. Burroughs" I said.

"Good Morning, Pauline Estelle—the girl with the melodious name." I smiled

"Where were we when we last spoke? I don't mean yesterday."

"You were asking about my father, Frederick Merry, wanting to know where he was."

"Oh yes," she said. "Do you have time to tell me about him this morning?"

"Yes, I do," I replied. ""He teaches English at Sumner. I live with him, and my mother, and sister Frederica, just down the street on Hammett Place."

"My, my!" she said. "I remember him from when we taught together at Tougaloo College in Mississippi. I am surprised I didn't know he was here in St. Louis. You'll have to tell him 'hello' for me."

"I will. Now I have to get going," I said and started to move off when she said, "Pauline Estelle, I wonder if I could ask a favor of you?"

"Um, sure, I guess so."

"Well," she said, "I have a little problem that I don't quite know how to handle and it's about...it's about.... Wait,

I'll tell you tomorrow. You get off to school now, and I'll see you in the morning."

Now I was thinking really hard, and asking myself, "What kind of problem does she have that she thinks I can help her with, me just a thirteen-year-old girl?"

All I said was "Okay, then, I'll see you in the morning." And I ran off to school.

All day I wondered what it was she wanted from me. What problem did she have that she needed my help with? House work, a sick friend, her back yard, church, food,.. what? Had she discerned my super powers?

Yes, I had super powers. And here is the list of my super powers:

- I can read well, play the piano well,

- Think through problems,

- Use the public library's card catalog,

- Fearlessly ride public transportation,

- Find my own way to the St. Louis Art Museum in Forest Park,

- Shop in department stores in downtown St. Louis for my mother,

- Go by public transportation out to Overland, MO.

I have a personal drive to succeed and do well. I had traveled back east to Maryland, Pennsylvania, and Washington D.C. I had been to Camp Atwater in North Brookfield, MA, a camp where middle class Black folk sent their children.

Those were the obvious ones that, up until now, I had kept to myself. But what about my super abilities—to see through walls, or the strength in my hands, or my ability to run really, really fast, or my extra sense of smell, or my ability to move objects by waving my hands. (Actually, I didn't really have these kinds of powers, but if I had, wouldn't *that* have been delicious!) Perhaps calling on any or all of these abilities would be useful, but I would have to keep my super powers to myself and wait and see just what it was that Mrs. Burroughs had in mind.

The next morning, a Thursday, Mrs. Burroughs was waiting for me and, upon seeing me at her gate, said "Pauline Estelle, here is my problem." And she started to tell me.

"Even though you are very young, you must know that colored people are not treated well in this country, not just in the South, but all over the country."

I nodded my head. I knew that I went to a segregated school, lived in a colored community, went to a colored church, but I really didn't know the reason why this all was; it just was. Maybe I was like a fish in a fish bowl who is not aware of the water. Sensing that this was going to be a rather long story, I said, "Mrs. Burroughs, ma'am, it is Thursday, and tomorrow is Friday. It sounds like what you are going to tell me will take more time than I have right now. I have to get to school soon, but I have an idea."

She said, "What is your idea?"

I said, "Because it seems like what you are going to tell me might take more time than I have before I need to get going to school. Maybe I should come by your house this Saturday or Sunday afternoon. If I come then, I won't have to run off anywhere, and we'd have more time to talk about your problem."

She looked closely at me and said, "Pauline Estelle, you are so right. When can you come?"

I said, "Either Saturday, after I get back from my piano lessons, or Sunday after church."

Then she asked, "Why don't you come this Saturday. What would be a good time for you?"

"How about 2 p.m.?"

"That's fine."

"I will see you this Saturday at 2 p.m. after my piano lesson."

She smiled in agreement and I ran off to school.

Saturday came. I went out to Overland for my piano lesson, returned home, had a sandwich for lunch and then told my mother that I was going to meet Valena at her house. And off I went, but really I went to meet Mrs. Burroughs.

I quickly got to her house just a little before 2 p.m. She was waiting for me, and she invited me to join her on her porch, which I did. It was still fairly warm outside even though it was getting on into October. I was wearing blue jeans, a plaid shirt, a brown sweater, a pretty brown and green head scarf, and penny loafers. She was wearing a pretty black and grey-striped dress. She had put a red flowered pin on her lapel, and in her hair she had tied a red ribbon at the top of her long braid.

She asked me about my week at school and my music lesson that morning.

"My music lesson was great. I practice every day and look forward to riding the bus out to Overland. And I like the time I spend with my teacher during my lesson."

I described my teacher, Agnes Murillo, a young white woman, as being someone I really liked. I felt comfortable with her and looked forward to seeing her every week.

Mrs. Burroughs listened attentively, then said, "It is excellent that you are having a positive experience with a white person. You know, that is not the case for many of us." She then launched into telling me why she wanted my help.

"I started telling you last week that even though you are very young, you must know that colored people are not treated well in this country, not just in the South, but all over the country." I nodded and she went on.

"We have been pretty timid about asking for change, but there are groups around that think change is needed and...."

I interrupted her, asking, "What kind of change?"

She said, "Well, Pauline Estelle, just look around you and think."

Hmm.... Frankly, I had to stop and scratch my head, because I lived in a very nice house on a tree-lined street. My home was nicely furnished. My father was a teacher and well-respected in the community. Our neighbors on Hammett Place and other places in or near the Ville were nice, and most had nice homes.

Although it was true that the Episcopal church we attended was colored as were all my schools, I could ride the public transportation trolleys and buses without having to "sit in the back of the bus." I realized that, yes, there were things that colored people could not do or places where we could not go, like the privately-owned Fox movie Theater, and the one legitimate theater.

And there were neighborhoods where we could not live and probably jobs that we could not have—although I didn't really think much about jobs. All I knew was that most things nice were white and we weren't allowed or included. But that didn't bother me all that much, so what was Mrs. Burroughs getting at?

I told her what I was thinking and that I really didn't see any need for change.

She sighed and said, "Well child, I am going to tell you some things, and what I am going to tell you will help you see why something has to be done, why changes have to be made."

I said to her, "Well, before you begin, Mrs. Burroughs, I have to let you know that I have to be home around 4 p.m. Otherwise my Mother might begin to worry."

Mrs. Burroughs said, "Of course. Let's talk until around 3:45 p.m. for starters and perhaps we can make this a weekly thing, on Saturday or Sunday. I need time to tell you how I am hoping that you'll be able to help me."

I agreed, saying that I could come visit her after church on Sundays. So there it was. We set a schedule for when I would come to her house—Saturdays after my piano lessons or Sunday after church. Mrs. Burroughs then began to tell me things about what it was like for Blacks in this country. I had had no idea.

She began asking me about why I thought I lived in a neighborhood with only colored people. I didn't have an answer. She asked me why I went to school with only Black kids. She asked me if I knew about the kinds of jobs most colored people had. I didn't have an answer to any of her questions. Then she asked, "Pauline Estelle, why can't you go to the Fox Theater?" Again, I didn't have a coherent answer. "Uhmm," was all I could say.

"My point exactly!" she said. "You don't know the answer to these questions, and you should." By the time we got to this point, I realized that it was getting close to the time when I needed to get going home. With some relief, I said, "Mrs. Burroughs, I think that I need to get going." She stopped mid-sentence and said, "Lord have mercy, child, it is getting late. I'll see you next weekend for our chat, and perhaps during the week, as you walk to school we will wave."

I agreed with her. As I started for home, I turned and said to her, "Thanks, Mrs. Burroughs. See you next week for our chat."

The next week after church, I had lunch and again told my mother that I was going to go see Valena. I wasn't sure how many times I could use Valena as a reason for leaving the house on a Sunday afternoon, particularly since fibbing hadn't been something I was use to doing, but I would worry about that later. In fact I thought that once I got a handle on what Mrs. Burroughs wanted, I could tell my mother.

The school week went fine in spite of my usual discomfort at being Mr. Merry's daughter, faltering in Latin and struggling with algebra, let alone trying to figure out who my friends were, what to wear, how my hair looked and would those pimples ever go away!? As I walked to school, some mornings Mrs. Burroughs was outside and other mornings not, but it didn't matter to me now that she and I had a method of corresponding—the note on her front screen. Now I had two weekly bright spots—my music lessons and now my meetings with Mrs. Burroughs.

The next Sunday that we met, Mrs. Burroughs continued quizzing me about what I knew about how colored people were treated. Eventually, she just started telling me about the treatment of Negroes in our city and throughout the United States. She quickly understood that I didn't know much.

Did I know, she asked me, about colored GIs not having access to the opportunity to go to college? Did I know that, if someone in my family needed to go to the hospital, they could not go to Barnes Hospital, or St. Vincent de Paul, or any other white hospital nearby? Did I know that segregated hospitals were the rule?

That meant we could only get care at Homer G. Phillips or People's Hospital. Did I know that colored people were often denied care at white hospitals? She said that she knew of a badly-injured man who, upon arriving at a white hospital, was denied care—because he was colored. A white doctor was reported to have said, "It doesn't matter—he's just a nigger."

I was shocked.

As she talked, I just kept shaking my head 'no' to every question and every situation that she described. I knew none of this.

We had about one or two more sessions where she continued to talk to me about being colored in this country. She told me about lynchings. Lynchings were public, social events for whites, but definitely fearful, deadly events for Negroes. Here I stopped her and asked for a drink of water.

While I knew lynchings were something really bad, I had to ask her what they were.

She looked at me as though I had come from another planet. "You don't know what lynchings are?" she asked incredulously?

I shook my head.

She told me.

She said that lynchings were extra-judicial. This means that the white people just took the law into their own hands and killed Black people. The whites were not held accountable for their actions. No judge had told them it was okay, and afterward no judge gave them any punishment for doing it.

She said that white folks had the freedom—and felt the need—to kill innocent Blacks for fun, as warnings, or for any other reason...because killing them was their right. It could happen to any Black person—any man, any woman or any child. The lynchings mostly happened in the Deep South.

How could I have really known any of that? I didn't live in the Deep South.

She also told me about the limitations on Blacks who traveled. It was a dangerous prospect for Blacks, in their own cars, or even on public transportation. She said something else I hadn't known, namely, that there was something called *The Green Book*. It was a directory of hotels and private homes that welcomed colored travelers, since they could not stay in white hotels. It made traveling a bit easier.

She told me that traveling by car was not without danger. Having a *Green Book* made it a little less so. I told her about the summer traveling by car back to St. Louis from Chestertown with my parents and little sister. We stayed at a colored lady's house in Indiana for one night. Now I guessed that my parents may have used information in a Green Book.

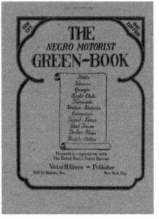

"I never asked them, but I betcha my folks used that, or some other source of information, about where colored people could stay."

Mrs. Burroughs said, "Yes, they probably did use a Green Book, or something like it." Then she asked, "Now, Pauline Estelle, what do you think of all this?"

"Well Mrs. Burroughs, I don't really know what to say. I never hear my parents talk about these kinds of things. They just seem to accept things, I guess. They don't seem angry or upset, or even to think that there is something they *can* do about any of the things you've told me."

Although, I can recall on occasion, my mother complaining about the treatment of colored people by whites. Mostly, it seemed as though she didn't think that anything could be done about it. I knew that she didn't like white people one bit. She, who was a lot lighter in skin color than I was, would on occasion speak about the deferential treatment lighter-skinned colored people would receive over darker-skinned Negroes. It would make her mad, but she didn't dwell on it.

Then it came to me; my parents, and many of the people they knew, all felt powerless to do anything about it. That was just the way things were, and all we could do was do the best we could.

"I am beginning to understand. My parents seem to think that all we *can* do is just do the best we can."

Mrs. Burroughs said, "And that's exactly my point!" I could almost hear the exclamation point in her voice. "That's exactly my point! Who says that we have to continue to live like this, under restrictions that are unfair, unjust, and unhealthy? You and I are fairly lucky, because we don't live in the Deep South."

"But, before I get to why I would like your help," she went on, "there's one more thing I want you to know about, and that's about the Great Migration. Do we have time to talk about it today?" she asked me.

I asked her, "What time is it? Will it would take long for you to tell me about it?"

She said, "I think that we should talk about it the next time you come. Next Saturday is it?" I said yes, thanked her for telling me all that she had, and said that I would see her next Saturday.

As I walked home, all the things that Mrs. Burroughs had told me that day and all the other things she had said all the other times we had met were churning around in my head. I felt excited, nervous, and I was beginning to feel that maybe I might have some *personal* power to actually *do something* about the unjust treatment of Blacks. I was excited to find out what would come next.

Frankly, I still had no real sense of being deprived. Just because I couldn't go to the Fox Theater didn't matter all that much to me. That I couldn't go to school with white kids didn't matter to me at all. That members of my community were denied access to jobs and health care and living in nice houses, this was nothing I had cared about, but should I?

It seemed that something was being revealed to me that I should care about, but I didn't know what it was just yet. I wasn't sure that I wanted a burden of that sort in my life. Still, I thought that I would give Mrs. Burroughs a chance to tell me. No adult had *ever* talked to me like she was talking to me. Not my parents, Uncle Ben and Aunt Irene or Aunt Carrie Bell, and definitely not my teachers.

As promised, we met again, but this time inside her house. The season was late fall and outside it was beginning to get really cold. This time, Mrs. Burroughs told me about the Great Migration.

Mrs. Burroughs told me that living conditions in the South for Blacks were, in a word, terrible, even for educated Blacks —the personal denigration, the poor living conditions, low wages, inferior schools and access to health care—every aspect of life was affected by bigoted Jim Crow laws. Segregated conditions were put in place by whites who did not, under any circumstances, want Blacks to have anything of value. Racism ruled everything. Racism shaped every law and every aspect of daily living.

Because most Blacks were easily identified by their skin color, they could not just fade away and disappear into the general white population. Our nappy hair and brown skin were our handcuffs. Rules and laws—white created— regulated how everyone lived, both whites and Blacks. So, to escape the suffocating, limiting, degrading racist limitations there, Black folks began to flee the South and went north or west.

The Great Migration started around 1910 and was still going on. Many Blacks moved from the South to major cities up North or West—among them New York, Chicago, and Los Angeles. Also, St. Louis, where my folks landed. Blacks in the South faced unending discrimination, unemployment and poverty. They were not allowed to start businesses and accumulate wealth and when they tried, so many obstacles were put into place that those trying would just give up. It was impossible to build wealth for their families. So, it was natural that many African American people migrated from South to North or West with a hope for better life.

I interrupted her saying, "Oh! This sounds like something I did several summers ago. I had noticed that a lot of the adults around me had moved to St. Louis from somewhere else, often from the South."

"How very interesting, Pauline Estelle. Tell me more."

"I decided, just for something to do, to ask a bunch of my neighbors some questions about why they came to St. Louis.

"Later, a young man named Joseph was in town doing some research for his Masters degree. He had found out that two artists who had worked in the WPA program for artists had moved to St. Louis and he wanted to interview them.

"When I told him what I had done—actually it was my mother who told him—he got all excited and asked me for details. Since I had kept notes on what all the grownups I'd talked to told me, he wanted to see them. Eventually he said he would put what I had done in his thesis as my contribution to the history of Negro Art of the WPA."

When I finished, Mrs. Burroughs said, "Wait a minute Pauline Estelle, you did what?"

"I talked to some of the grown ups near where I lived and I asked them why they had come to St. Louis."

"You are one amazing little girl. You already know something about what I was going to tell you about the

Great Migration. But my goodness, you discovered it on your own, only you didn't know it was called that. Didn't your parents tell you that the movement was called The Great Migration?"

"They might have, but I don't remember if they did."

"Well, it doesn't matter if they did or not, what matters is that on your own, you found out about the movement, even if you didn't call it that. So I am going to tell you more about it. My goodness, you are just a wonder," she said smiling at me.

As she began telling me about the Great Migration, she confirmed what I was already beginning to understand about being a Negro in the United States.

Mrs. Burroughs continued describing life in the South for Blacks. She said that Blacks enjoyed few, if any, civil and political rights. Black people and white people did not have public lives together, except under Jim Crow restrictions. More than a million Black soldiers fought in World War II, but she said that those who came from the South could not vote. Blacks who tried to register faced the possibility of beatings, loss of job, loss of credit, or eviction from their land. Lynchings still occurred and Jim Crow laws enforced segregation of the races in street cars, trains, hotels, restaurants, hospitals, recreational facilities and employment.

Even arriving in the North did not guarantee us social freedom, Mrs. Burroughs explained. The racism could be almost as brutal and unforgiving as it was in the South, but it seemed that the air was easier to breathe, the restrictions fewer, and access to a better life seemed to be a real possibility.

This means, my parents, and the parents of all my friends at school and church, and thousands of others I would never know, were migrants.

Migrations to flee unbearable conditions or seeking better opportunities have happened throughout history and continue today. For more than a century now, some of them were Mexicans coming to what they call "Los Estados Unidos." After the Vietnam war the largest group of Vietnamese outside of Viet Nam are now living in Westminster, CA. And amid the wars in the Middle East and in Ukraine, yet more migrants are flooding into Europe and the United States.

The stories are the same, yet different. All were fleeing for their lives from despotic, racist regimes or intolerable living conditions with the hope of better futures. Most times it worked, but some restrictions still existed for all of these groups looking for better lives.

One result of the large number of Blacks who migrated from the South to New York City was that they formed a community within the city, called Harlem. It is much like The Ville in St. Louis.

There were many different kinds of Black people in Harlem, including at one point my father who lived in Harlem while attending Columbia University to get his Masters degree. Later, my mother worked at Harlem Hospital.

And there were many artists of all kinds (painters, poets, actors, musicians, and more) living in Harlem. This resulted in an explosion of artistic activity now called the Harlem Renaissance.

One of them was Langston Hughes, who became very famous worldwide. Perhaps my favorite of his poems, is one he wrote in 1949, called "One Way Ticket."

In it he describes the frustration felt by many Blacks living under the oppressive Jim Crow laws, the threat of lynchings, and the general cruelty and fearfulness of even the whites in the South, and the desperation of the Blacks for some escape, no matter where. He longs for a one-way ticket to somewhere, anywhere else.

Another member of the Harlem Renaissance movement, and a friend of Langston Hughes, was Jacob Lawrence. He worked for the Works Projects Administration (that I told you about in my story, Where Have You Been") creating a series of 60 paintings describing his observations of "The Great Migration" which is the common term for the mass migration of Blacks from the South to the north and west.

The Museum of Modern Art in New York city has published a wonderful book detailing how Lawrence created his 'The Migration Series, and showing images of those paintings[4].

The first of his paintings, often called "Panel 1," shows a railroad ticket office with three windows, a crowd of colored people standing in line in front of each of them, and with signs over the windows saying, "Chicago," "New York," and "St. Louis." This image reminds me of what Mr. Moore told me, as you may recall reading in my story, "Where Have You Been?"

The migration spanned the period for 1910 to 1970, and it turns out that I became a part of it when I left Missouri for California in 1959. You can learn a lot more about The Great Migration in Isabel Wilkerson's wonderful book, "The Warmth of Other Suns."

I fled to California three days after I graduated from The University of Missouri, Columbia. Some of what you have just read is what I learned from Mrs. Burroughs then. Much later in my life, I learned a great deal more from many sources. One of the best is an extraordinary account of The Great Migration in Isabel Wilkerson's book "The Warmth of Other Suns."

---

[4] Jacob Lawrence, *The Great Migration Series, The Museum of Modern Art*; Library of Congress Control Number: 2014957848

At our next get together, Mrs. Burroughs said that it was time to move on to the project for which she was soliciting my help. She said, "But before we start, do you have any thoughts about what I've told you so far?"

It was a cool, fall Saturday afternoon; there was a mild breeze and the smell of burning leaves filled the air. I'd had another enjoyable piano lesson that morning. I was wearing a warm brown plaid jacket and a brown skirt that I liked. My hair, as usual, had been recently pressed and I thought it looked nice. I felt relaxed as I remembered how things had gone for me at school. It had been a pretty good week.

I was beginning to be included in a group of kids who, as it turns out, would still be a part of my life as adults. In fact, my first husband and his twin sisters were in that group, and we are still friends.

I said to Mrs. Burroughs that I had given some thought to what she had said (How could I not?). I was beginning to appreciate the circumstances that affected my life, even though, as I insisted, my life was quite nice.

She said, "Yes, many of our lives are quite nice, but there is much room for improvement. To improve our lives and the lives of others will require action by those who see the inequalities and want to do something to change them."

She pointed out that there were a lot of people who thought that the treatment of colored people in the country was disgraceful, and that something should be done to make their lives better. She said that some of them were beginning to organize with the intention of making changes.

Finally Mrs. Burroughs told me what she wanted me to do. She wanted me to help her—me, a thirteen year old—with the organization "The Congress of Racial Equality," commonly known as CORE. The people who started it were a mixed racial group of graduate students at the University of Chicago. CORE was established by James Farmer in 1942 to improve race relations and end discriminatory policies through direct-action projects.

Mrs. Burroughs told me a story about Mahatma Gandhi (the famous Indian lawyer and civil rights activist), when traveling by train in South Africa, he encountered a white man who demanded that Gandhi leave the car reserved for whites and take a seat with the other Coloreds. That demand that he move to another car, was what galvanized Gandhi to start the move to get India out from under British rule and to challenge white privilege. Mrs. Burroughs said that the founders of CORE were inspired by Mahatma Gandhi's protest strategies of nonviolence and civil disobedience.

I still didn't quite understand what she wanted me to help her with. Was this the problem that she wanted my help with? I thought, she must be crazy, but of course I didn't even think to say that, or challenge her. Finally, I said, "What? You want me to help you do what?"

She laughed out loud and said, "Yes, Pauline Estelle, I want *you* to help us make some changes in how colored people are treated in this country. You might be young, but you are smart and, I think, courageous." (Perhaps she was thinking about how I went alone every Saturday to my piano lessons out in Overland, where no Black people lived.) "Your youthful presence will be a great asset to the St. Louis CORE chapter. We are practicing civil disobedience."

The word disobedience really caught my attention. "You want me to do something that is wrong?" I asked her.

She emphatically replied, "Absolutely! That's the whole point. We want to bring attention to inequities by physically challenging rules, regulations, and practices that keep colored people down."

She did not go into other ways these practices would be challenged—like the courts—but these local and public activities would bring attention to our situations, visibly and publicly. They would include people of different races, and they would not be waiting for approval. These ordinary activists would be doing things without permission, in the face of white people who would object.

'*Oh my goodness,*' I thought to myself.

"This is quite a lot for me to take in."

She said, "Well, I'm not surprised. That's why I took the time to tell you a bit of history, giving you some background about why we will be doing things to bring about change in the face of opposition, and perhaps danger. After all, Black folks are still being lynched with impunity." Hmmm, impunity. A lovely new word for me, I thought. Then, what she just told me registered and out loud, I blurted:

"Still being lynched!"

"Yes, lynchings are still going on," she repeated, "but we can talk about that another time. Right now, I want to know if you'll join us?"

I pulled at my bangs, ran my fingers over my pressed hair and thought to myself, '*How could I not join?*' even though I still didn't quite get the whole picture, or even know exactly what I'd be doing. I thought that, somehow, being involved in this would give me the opportunity to use some of my super powers, and I wouldn't be so worried about my life at Sumner.

"Yes, I'll do it!" I declared to Mrs. Burroughs. We both laughed and smiled at each other for seemingly no reason, but I felt that I now had something of my own in which I could be me, Pauline Estelle Merry, and not Mr. Merry's daughter.

Before I headed home, Mrs. Burroughs and I agreed on the day and time of our next meeting.

As I walked home, I thought that now would be the time to let my mother know what I had been up to on Saturday and Sunday afternoons for the past couple of months or so.

"Mother Dear," I called to her when I got home, "Where are you?" Even though our house was small, calling out to her was just what I did when I got home. She was in the kitchen making dinner. We ate early on Saturdays and it was about time for us to sit down and eat. I set the table for dinner. We ate off of Willow Blue plates and my mother, wearing a pretty gray and yellow dress, insisted on using her sterling silver forks, knives and spoons at every meal.

"How was your day," she asked, "and by the way, where have you been? It's late." Perfect, here was the time for me to tell her what I had been doing on Saturday and Sunday afternoons for the past several months.

I began to tell her about Mrs. Burroughs and my weekly visits with her on St. Ferdinand, starting with my early contact with her as I walked to school. I told her how those sessions evolved to my Saturday and Sunday meetings.

As I talked, my father and sister joined us at the table. My father said grace, good Episcopalians that we were, and we began to eat. There was no baseball game to listen to so both my father and sister had nothing to do over dinner, but listen to me tell my mother what had been happening. Even though the meetings with Mrs. Burroughs had taken place over several months, I was able to tell them most all that she had told me and what she and I had talked about. They all sat very still and just looked at me.

My father said, "Hmmm." My mother said, "Hmmm." My sister said nothing.

And after a bit, my father said "Well" and my mother said "Hmmm."

I was more than a little nervous, because I had no idea what they would say. So I just sat there, waiting and poking at the meringue on my slice of lemon pie.

Finally my mother said, "Well, this is all very interesting, Pauline Estelle. So you weren't really at Valena's all these times?"

"Well, I was there once or twice, but most of the time I was at Mrs. Burroughs' after my piano lessons or after church."

She looked at my father, smiling, and said, "Well Fritz, we've got quite a young lady here. Meeting with an adult we don't know, planning meetings with her and getting there without either of us being involved."

My father, being the stricter of the two, wasn't so ready to provide his support, but after a bit said, "Well, tell us more."

"The most important thing to me is that she wants me to help the St. Louis CORE group and I... and I want to." This was perhaps the most radical thing I had ever said to my parents in my entire life up to then.

I took the chance of having their disapproval laid upon me, They might say "No, Pauline Estelle, you can't do it. Whatever it is she wants you to do, or whatever CORE does —"

Before they got the chance to say anything, I said, "Oh, I forgot to tell you, Daddy, she knows you. Mrs. Burroughs says you two taught at Tougaloo College, together. She didn't know that you were here in St. Louis, and I was supposed to tell you that she sends her greetings. So, Mrs. Burroughs says hello."

"Mrs. who?" my father asked.

"Mrs. Burroughs," I replied. He sat there, mulling, over what I had said. Finally he smiled and said, "Is her first name Eva? Oh, yes then, I do remember her. A very tall, slender, light-skinned woman? She wore her hair in a long braid back then."

"Yes, that's right," I said. I was relieved that he remembered her, and she was still wearing her hair in a long braid. My father went on to say that they had both taught English at Tougaloo, but that he had not liked the Deep South, and he decided to move back North where he felt safer and freer. This was before he had met my mother. With this knowledge, of who I had been spending many Saturdays and Sundays with, he visibly relaxed.

My mother said, "Fritz, I think Pauline Estelle should be able to do what Mrs. Burroughs is asking." Clearly, my mother had also relaxed, probably because his knowing Mrs. Burroughs made it easier for her to say this to him. I think she thought it would be good for me.

After more discussion, they said that I could join Mrs. Burroughs in the CORE activities.

I said, "I'll let you know what she wants me to do, before I do it." Thus began my active participation in civil disobedience.

The civil rights movement gained momentum while I was growing up in the 50s, even if it wasn't as visible then as it later became. Looking back, I am sure that our work helped establish the groundwork for the even more extensive movement in the 1960s.

I went to many meetings with Mrs. Burroughs where strategy was discussed. She introduced me to the group as her young friend and Frederick Merry's daughter. Some of them knew him, but most didn't.

Sometimes these meetings were in the evenings after school, but many were held Saturday or Sunday afternoons, which met with my parents' approval. On occasion I had to miss church or my music lessons. And depending on the season, I wore one of my school outfits—usually a blouse, sweater and a brown or navy blue skirt to CORE meetings. Plaid was a popular fabric for skirts, and I had several plaid skirts that I loved to wear with a horse pin pinned to the front, about half way down the length of the skirt. And my shoes were either penny loafers or brown saddle shoes worn with white socks.

I have already given you some idea of where Blacks lived in St. Louis, but I think I need to say a bit more about how access to housing worked for us then. Racial covenants were the rule. Racial covenants were legal documents that forbad the owners of property from selling, leasing, or renting it to specified groups— in this case, Negroes. Because of them, there were neighborhoods where my family and I could not live and the extension of that is that we also couldn't eat in certain places, go to schools with white kids, or attend movies where whites went, unless we sat in the balcony.

The Ville was the Black middle-class neighborhood of St. Louis. CORE wanted to extend our opportunities in housing and access, and to other things in general that white folks did without question. Simple as that. One of our early successes was that several restaurants changed their policies after CORE sit-ins. Then we had a few nice restaurants where we could eat with whites.

In all, from 1950-54, the years I was at Sumner, we participated in over 50 civil rights actions that extended our access to places where before we were forbidden. That doesn't seem like a lot, but, as the saying goes, you have to start somewhere.

CORE, The Congress of Racial Equality, was not the only group working for minority civil rights. Here in the USA, the most well-known is the NAACP: The National Association for the Advancement of Colored People, founded in 1903. Although people of African descent were, by far, the largest group in the United States that challenged rules designed to limit civil rights, other nonwhite groups were also unjust targets of racial intolerance.

Japanese residents in California had been viciously, unceremoniously, and wrongly removed from their homes in California during WW II. The infamous Executive Order 9066 issued on February 19, 1942 sent Japanese residents, many of whom were United States citizens, to detention camps. Although they had done nothing to deserve such treatment except be of

Japanese descent, it was a panic response to the December 7, 1941 unexpected bombing of Pearl Harbor. The order authorized the evacuation of all persons deemed a potential threat to national security from the West Coast to relocation centers further inland.

But Blacks and the Japanese were not the only non-whites groups to suffer discrimination. Chinese immigrants in San Francisco suffered from unmentionable hate crimes—simply because they were Chinese. From Seattle to Los Angeles, from Wyoming to the small towns of California, immigrants from China were forced out of business, run out of town, beaten, tortured, lynched, and massacred, usually with little hope of help from the law.

However, the largest group who suffered the most was the Native Americans who had their lands out-right stolen after which they were sent to what could be called "concentration camps," but were euphemistically called "reservations." Millions of their descendants still live on reservations.

*The land that was stolen actually includes **all** of the United States. America was born out of attempted genocide, theft, and slave labor and we are still dealing with the attitudes and circumstances that accompany such terrible behavior, often trying to justify even it as it continues.*

Fortunately, many whites are joining with those of us who have been the target of these unjust actions in protesting for the cause of equality, replacing those unjust institutions with more humane ones. You can find more about the injustices to various non-white groups in this country by going to library resources or on the web.

As I was working with Mrs. Burroughs, I wondered aloud to her one day what was the source of such awful attitudes toward us. Well, she said that basically it goes back to beliefs held by white slave holders who believed that in order to maintain their power, they had to find a way to justify looking down on their enslaved Africans and their descendants. Those attitudes and behaviors extended to anyone who was not white. They continually claimed that their enslaved Africans and African-Americans were less than human, and they did this in order to maintain their superior status economically and in all other ways.

Colored people had to be made less than human and therefore not worthy of rights and institutions that would make them whole. Here is a rather long quote from John C Calhoun. He presented his ideas more than one hundred years before my birth. This statement, I believe, is representative of attitudes, laws and practices that ensued, causing unequal rights for colored people.

"We of the South will not, cannot surrender our institutions. To maintain the existing relations between the two races inhabiting that section of the Union is indispensable to the peace and happiness of both. It cannot be subverted without drenching the country in blood and extirpating one or the other of the races. Be it good or bad, it has grown up with our society and institutions and is so interwoven with them that to destroy it would be to destroy us as a people. But let me not be understood as admitting, even by implication, that the existing relations between the two races, in the slaveholding states, is an evil. Far otherwise; I hold it to be a good, as it has thus far proved itself to be, to both, and will continue to prove so, if not disturbed by the fell spirit of Abolition.

"I appeal to facts. Never before has the Black race of Central Africa, from the dawn of history to the present day, attained a condition so civilized and so improved, not only physically but morally and intellectually. It came among us in a low, degraded, and savage condition, and, in the course of a few generations, it has grown up under the fostering care of our institutions, as reviled as they have been, to its present comparative civilized condition. This, with the rapid increase of numbers, is conclusive proof of the general happiness of the race, in spite of all the exaggerated tales to the contrary."

This argument appealed to plantation owners. It appealed to whites who were threatened by any advancement colored people would or could make. They agreed that keeping them down was the order of the day. It also appealed to financiers who needed slave labor to supply the necessary labor to harvesting cotton, which was such an important crop economically that it was sometimes referred to as "King Cotton."

Yet, we colored people have survived the mistreatment with dignity and hope, and we made—and continue to make—substantial contributions to this country. And in some places, we even thrived, but not enough, as I was learning. In the 50s, we still had many, many miles to go.

* * * * *

As it turned out, I did okay at Sumner, after my disastrous first semester. I was elected to be a member of the Student Council, and I joined the Human Relations Club and the Rhythmic Club. But nothing that happened to me at school had as much impact on my life as my piano lessons, and CORE.

Sumner was... well it was Sumner. It was a safe place, with kind thoughtful teachers who wanted us to succeed. In fact, many of those teachers had fine educations themselves, having gone to white universities as well as HBUCs (Historically Black Universities & Colleges). And while I was not especially popular, my circle of friends were the smart kids.

CORE gave me an opportunity to enlarge my world, and it was *my* thing. I sat in at white drug store lunch counters. I went to white movie houses. I shopped and tried on clothes at department stores. Along with Mrs. Burroughs, I attended white Episcopal churches.

I also went to the Episcopal Diocesan church camp for several summers. During my first time at the camp, which was located in the Ozarks, the girls gathered in the girls' sleeping quarters to get acquainted. I was the only colored girl there. After some time spent telling one another about our schools, activities and courses, and our lives in general, we went outside and walked toward the lake front.

Somehow, I got separated from the white girls and when I saw them again, coming toward me as a group, I panicked. I could not for the life of me tell one girl from the other—they all looked alike!

Eventually, I got to know them as individuals, but recalling that moment, of not being able to distinguish one girl from another, amuses me when I hear of whites not being able to tell Black folks apart.

As a part of my CORE activities, I went to other white churches that were expressing an interest in civil rights. I went to lectures about racial equality. At the CORE planning sessions, I learned from grown-ups about the need for civil rights, even before the Civil Rights Movement of the late 50s and early 60s, and I learned how these needs could be translated into civil actions. It was exciting. I also think that using my super powers —reading, not being afraid to go places, feeling comfortable, and using the public library with ease—all that made my work with CORE easy. The grown-ups were impressed and I was happy.

Frankly, what I wanted for myself was to be important in the world. Many years later, a fellow instructor at a community college where I was a dean after I left the field of nursing, said to me in an accusatory tone of voice, "Well, you always wanted to be somebody." My goodness, how did he know? He had just met me, but he was right. I did want to be somebody, and my CORE activities helped lay a foundation that gave me self-assurance, pride in being a part of something important, and a can-do attitude that I have used to my benefit, all of my life.

I graduated from Sumner, in June, 1954, and guess what? It was *my* name that appeared in the *St. Louis Post Dispatch* as having had perfect attendance for four years. There was

no mention of the National Honor Society (NHS) or of any of the kids who were NHS members —even though my father had so very much wanted me to be a NHS member.

Here is a picture of the girls that I was closest to at Sumner, taken in 1954 after the Baccalaureate services at All Saints Episcopal Church the Sunday before our graduation. Except for me, at the left, they were all members of the NHS. The others, left to right, are: Valena Broussard, Eleanor Casey, Dorothy Beckwith and Frances Denny (kneeling).

And I did as well as any of them as an adult. I know because I am still in contact with some of them. So there you go! My father's worries were unnecessary.

Sometimes the things you think are so important in the moment turn out not to be at all important later on.

Some Questions to Think About

1. When you are going to school, what do you wear? Are you required to wear a uniform? And how are you likely to dress for a special occasion?

2. Do you enjoy changing of seasons where you live? What is your favorite season, and why? (Do you participate in any seasonal sports?)

3. Do you ever get to spend time alone? Often enough? When you are alone are there some things you especially like to do? Like what?

4. Has anyone ever asked you to help out on a Project? Would you say 'yes' if you could? Is there a Project you've heard about that you would really like to work on? Have you thought about what you might learn while doing that?

5. What do you understand about "racial segregation"? How did you first learn about it?

6. Racial segregation is just one kind of "prejudice" (*to pre-judge*. Can you think of other kinds? Have you experienced any form of prejudice in your life?

7. How would you explain to a classmate—or to a good friend—what Civil Rights are?

8. Who are your Civil Rights Heroes?

9. Are you planning to go to college? Why, or why not? What do you have to do to get there?

✱ ✱ ✱ ✱ ✱

If You Want to Learn More
Here are some good sources of information:

You can read all about Charles Sumner's beating in the official records of the U. S. Senate:
https://www.senate.gov/artandhistory/history/minute/The_C aning_of_Senator_Charles_Sumner.htm

To learn more about the Harlem Renaissance you might look at: https://www.history.com/topics/roaring-twenties/harlem-renaissance, or https://en.wikipedia.org/wiki/Harlem_Renaissance.

To learn more about Langston Hughes, see https://www.studysmarter.us/explanations/history/us-history/langston-hughes/.

And for his poem, One-Way Ticket, see https://www.google.com/url?sa=t&rct=j&q=&esrc=s&source=web&cd=&cad=rja&uact=8&ved=2ahUKEwi51p_Suvf5AhXVk2oFHRmGA3AQFnoECBAQAQ&url=https%3A%2F%2Fnationalhumanitiescenter.org%2Fows%2Fseminars%2Ftcentury%2Fgmigration%2FHughes_OneWayTicket.pdf&usg=AOvVaw2bc06fCqGfptGMtb59WZlU.

Aaron Douglas was another of the Harlem Renaissance artists. At this website you can learn about a 1936 show he created to demonstrate that African-American art was just as good as any European art: https://www.washingtonpost.com/arts-entertainment/interactive/2022/aaron-douglas-into-bondage/

Sue Monk Kidd, *The Invention of Wings*, A searing and soaring story of two women bound together as mistress and slave.

Henry Louis Gates, Jr., *Stony the Road: Reconstruction, white Supremacy, and the Rise of Jim Crow*

This link tells the story of Ghandi's epiphany very nicely: https://www.sahistory.org.za/dated-event/mk-gandhi-forcibly-removed-whites-only-train-carriage

I'd love to hear from you, my readers.
You may contact me, the author, by emailing
me at:
PaulineEstelleMerry@GreatTalesToldWell.com

Epilogue

Beginning with "Kindergarten Through Eighth Grade," "Seeing the 'Greats' with My Mother," and "Where Have You Been," followed by "Summer Time" and "Sumner High", you have journeyed with me, Pauline Estelle, as I was growing up—all the way from Kindergarten through graduating from high school. I made discoveries about my family, my community, my St. Louis, and some of my favorite vacation places but, most importantly, I made discoveries about myself. I was smart, curious, and fearless. I used what I learned in those growing up years to became a happy and successful adult.

After getting my Bachelors of Science in Nursing (BSN) from The University of Missouri, Columbia, I started working as a nurse, but I quickly found out that nursing was not for me. Actually, I had already realized that when I was a senior, but at that point in my college education I felt it was too late to change my major. Once I was in the real world, I learned that nursing definitely was not what I wanted to do. Having come from a family full of educators, and at my mother's prompting, I chose to also become an educator.

Making that change was an act of bravery. It required me to endure quite a bit of sacrifice. My husband objected, and I had a son to care for. I went to school in the day to earn my teaching credential, slept in the afternoon and worked as a nurse at night. It was not easy, but after five long years, I began my life as a teacher. And I ended up having a long and satisfying career in education.

Soon after I started teaching, I decided to continue my education further and get a doctoral level degree (a Ph.D.). To get that degree, I found out I needed to prove my competence in two languages. I ended up choosing Advanced Statistics for one, and French for the other. To help me with the French, and because I wanted a new car, I flew to Frankfort, Germany, picked up a Karmann Ghia convertible and drove with my son down to Nice, France to study. It never occurred to me to be afraid to go alone with my son. My second husband had no objections. When I was done in Nice, I drove us to Copenhagen and at the end of that trip I dropped my car in Munich to be shipped to LA, and we flew home.

On several other occasions, I went off alone to Mexico to study Spanish. I saw only maybe one or two Black people the entire time I was there. I lived with Mexican families, studied in language schools, walked unaccompanied in Guadalajara, Mexico City and Curenavaca and rode the local buses.

On a trip I took to work as a volunteer teacher in Arusha, Tanzania, in Africa, when I arrived at the Kilimanjaro Airport in Tanzania, the official looking at my passport said,

"You are 75 years old."

"Yes I am."

"And you are alone?"

"Yes"

He said, "Seventy-five year old women don't travel alone." (My age, it turns out, was of special interest because at that time the life span of men in Tanzania was 52. The life span of women was 54. To them and, apparently, to this customs agent, I was a wonder.)

"Well I do."

The next day I found myself on the back of a motorcycle, squeezed between the driver and a guide, both of whom I had just met.

While riding along the bumpy road to hike to a hidden waterfall, I said to myself, "No one in the whole wide world knows where I am!"

And I was quite all right with that.

And, I'm still fearless.

I'm a feisty, 85-year-old woman who loves art and music, and who also celebrates (on this T-shirt) the women who have been or are Justices on the United States Supreme Court. If only there were even more!

Epilogue

Notes on the Maps, Photos, and Design

Whenever I read a story, I imagine what the people I am reading about look like, and where the places I read about are in relation to one another.

When the stories are, like mine, about real people and real places, I'm unlikely to imagine either the people or the places accurately. Now it may not matter to you if what you imagine is true or not. But you might like some help making your imaginings a bit closer to reality.

So, I've included a number of pictures in this book to give you just that sort of help. And I've also included four maps. The next section is meant to help you understand what those maps show and where the images that form the background of those maps came from.

Maps

Making a map is often a bit tricky. Making a map about somewhere as it was most of century ago can be even trickier. But, I've done the best I can.

Almost all of the places you will find mentioned in one or more of my stories can be located on at least one of the four maps in this book.

The first map, "My Ville," shows you all the streets in and around The Ville and many of the key places there as they were back when my stories took place in the 1940s and 1950s. Any place that is mentioned in one of my stories that fits on this map is labeled as such.

In the background of this map you actually see all the streets and some of the major buildings or park areas, etc. as they are now in 2022, but the highlighted spots and their labels tell you about how it was back in the time of my stories.

The background images in all of these maps, are taken from screen images of the mapping program Google Earth Pro for those locations.

The second map, "My St. Louis," shows you the all the places mentioned in my stories in the entire city of St. Louis plus some of the surrounding areas including several of the smaller cities that surround St. Louis. (Only the two of those smaller cities that are mentioned in my stories are identified by name on this map.)

The third map, "My Country," shows almost all of the United States and a bit of both Mexico and Canada. Here you see labeled all of the key locations I mention in my stories.

The fourth map, "My World," shows all the places I mention in my stories from St. Louis near the western edge of the map, to the east coast of the USA, and on across the Atlantic Ocean to Europe. On this map I've highlighted two of the states, Missouri and Alabama, since they are both mentioned prominently in my stories.

Photos

About half of the photos in this book are either ones that were taken when these stories took place, or earlier, or they are recent photos my husband and I took while we were traveling to those locations. Those old family photos I've carried around all the years since, came in handy when I decided to write this book.

The other photos are either from a public website or other public document, or they are Google Street View images of the designated location.

A few of the photos deserve a bit more of an explanation.

The front cover has two photographic images on it. *The obvious one in the center is a photo taken in 1942 showing me and my younger sister all dressed* *up and sitting on the front steps of our house on St. Ferdinand.*

The brown background on the cover is actually another photograph—in this case of a portion of my back taken in 2022, showing just what shade of brown skin this "little Black girl" has.

The photo on page 16 of the house at 4718 Hammet Place *shows you how it looks now (well how it looked in a Google Street View in 2021). The most important things missing in that image are the lovely trees I recall from when I lived there.*

Here is a photo taken in the early 1960s. In this photo I am standing in front of that house with my son. My father didn't aim the camera at the house, but rather down the street, thus showing the lovely trees all along the block. That's what I remember so fondly,  *and when we saw the current Google Street view of the house I was really saddened to discover that many of those trees have been taken down.*

The photos of Pauline Merry and Grace Bumbry *on page 35 are copied from my copy of my 1954 graduating class yearbook, "The Maroon and White." That also is the source for the* **Sumner High School faculty event** *shown on page 153.*

The family tree diagram on page 147 is redrawn from a portion of a diagram in a letter I received in 2010.

Design

Most of the headings, the front matter, and most of the body text (the portion of the body text representing what the young Pauline Estelle is saying) is set in a very easy to read serif font called Bodoni MT. *Occasionally, especially for things the young Pauline Estelle quotes, an italic version of Bodoni MT is used.*

For contrast, the adult author's comments (and most of these Notes on Maps, Photos, and Design) are set in a sans serif font called Verdana italic.

The "White Man's Declaration of Independence" (pp 21-23) is set in another sans serif font called Estrangelo Edessa italic.

The maps and the general style of the book were created by John M. Goodman, my husband.

CPSIA information can be obtained
at www.ICGtesting.com
Printed in the USA
BVHW062339141222
654221BV00008B/144

9 798987 199701